What they're saying about *The Gus Chronicles I*

"*The Gus Chronicles I* is as powerful an experience now as it was when first published in 1994. Gus takes the reader on an inside-out journey through the world of residential treatment, and does so with raw emotional energy, wit, and devastatingly accurate observation about all of us adult caretakers. Charles Appelstein's gift is that he uses Gus's voice to make the most complicated ideas readily accessible. *The Gus Chronicles I* is, quite simply, the perfect book for training youth care professionals at all levels of experience. If you are in the business of taking care of other people's children, I highly recommend getting to know Gus."

Rick Small, Ph.D., CEO, Walker Home School

"Choosing to use *The Gus Chronicles I* as the first reading assignment in my Introduction to Psychology course this past fall was the best decision I could have made. As it happened, this book was the perfect way to introduce some of the major terms and concepts, as well as serious themes and theories of psychology. After working with Gus, students became enthusiastic and gained confidence in their ability to analyze and apply the concepts raised here to other contexts. This book appeals to a wide range of student learning styles and levels. I am very glad I decided to adopt it and strongly recommend it as a motivational source to supplement any psychology text."

Claire Cummings, Ph.D.
Former psychology instructor, Newbury College

"Charlie Appelstein has portrayed Gus in a thoroughly believable account of an abused and troubled youth. Gus's recollections of his first day in residential care were so chilling to me that I quickly forgot Gus was not real."

John R. Seita, Ph.D.
Program director, Kellogg Youth Initiative Partnerships

"Every August, I reread *The Gus Chronicles I*. It serves as an important reminder that everyone has a story and that story has an impact on the way we see and function within our world. Gus naturally elicits empathy from his readers. *The Gus Chronicles I* should be read by all who work with and care for children."

Jenne Flewelling, M.Ed.
Principal, North Beverly Elementary School, Beverly, MA

"*The Gus Chronicles I* is required reading at the college I attended. It remains on the bookshelf in my office, where I use it to refocus when I lose sight of why I do residential care."

Jessica Lusk
President, Manitoba Child and Youth Care Workers'
Association

THE GUS CHRONICLES I

Reflections from an Abused Kid

CHARLES D. APPELSTEIN, M.S.W.

(and Gus E. Studelmeyer)

Updated and Revised Edition

APPELSTEIN TRAINING RESOURCES

Salem, New Hampshire

Published by:

Appelstein Training Resources
12 Martin Ave.
Salem, NH 03079
www.charliea.com

Editor: Ellen Kleiner

Book design and production: Angela Werneke

Cover and interior art: Maureen Burdock

Appelstein Training Resources provides original strength-based training, consultation, and literature to programs, schools, and parent associations nationwide to assist in understanding and responding to the challenging behavior of children and youth.

Printed in the United States of America on recycled paper

Publisher's Cataloging-in-Publication Data

Appelstein, Charles D.

The Gus chronicles I : reflections from an abused kid / Charles D. Appelstein (and Gus E. Studelmeyer). — Upd. and rev. ed. — Salem, N.H. : Appelstein Training Resources, c2012.

    p. ; cm.

    ISBN: 978-0-9719640-2-0
First published in 1994 under title: The Gus chronicles : reflections from an abused kid : about sexual & physical abuse, residential treatment, foster care, family unification, and much more (Needham, Mass. : Albert E. Trieschman Center, c1994).

    Summary: Challenges professionals to look at residential care from the perspective of a 13-year old boy and to respond to the obstacles he faces.

    1. Abused children—Fiction. 2. Child abuse—Fiction. 3. Abused children—Psychology. 4. Abused children—Rehabilitation. 5. Didactic fiction. I. Appelstein Training Resources. II. Title.

PS3551.P5577 G87 2011   2009911536

813.54--dc22   110

1 3 5 7 9 10 8 6 4 2

To the memory of my father, Edward Appelstein ~

a dad Gus should have had ~

and

to Floyd Alwon, Ed.D.,

former director of the Walker-Trieschman Center,

a division of the Child Welfare League of America,

a remarkable advocate for at-risk kids and

the encouragement for bringing The Gus Chronicles I

to print in its original edition.

CONTENTS

FOREWORD

A good story can be more powerful than experience, for it lures us into the inner worlds of people we otherwise would not have the opportunity to know. When I picked up *The Gus Chronicles I*, I was transported back to the time I served as a counselor in a summer camp for troubled Detroit kids who acted like Gus. My coworkers and I were young, idealistic, and armed with some baccalaureate behavioral theory— but little practice wisdom. Without the script of these youths' secret battle plan, we could not decode their hostile behavior. Veteran adult-fighters, they responded to our friendly gestures with X-rated words and warlike acts. In an impressive show of reverse behavior modification, the campers transformed the counselors, sucking us into conflict cycles and counter-aggression.

Had we been able to read a book like *The Gus Chronicles I*, then perhaps we could have deciphered the hurt buried beneath the hate. This book is for anyone who wants deeply to understand and help angry, adult-wary youth. Unless we have personally experienced severe abuse, we cannot imagine how deep its wounds can be. In *Gus*, we see how much courage it takes to learn to trust again, and how hard adults must work to be worthy of that trust.

—Larry Brendtro
President, Reclaiming Children and Youth

INTRODUCTION

My name is Gus E. Studelmeyer. I'm a fictitious teenage character. I think that stinks.

How would you like to live inside of a damn book? Me, I want to live. I want to taste things.

I want to have sex! I was created sometime during 1990. The author got some wonderful inspiration one night and . . . voilà . . . Gus E. Studelmeyer, at your service.

After creating me, the author asked me to write an essay about life in residential treatment. He thought it would be cool for people to get a look at residential treatment from an abused kid's perspective. At first, I turned him down. I didn't like the fact that he made me pudgy with red hair and zits. But being fictitious made me what one might call a weak negotiator. So I wrote the darn essay and disappeared.

Three months go by and—bang—the dude shows up again, asking me to write a follow-up essay. This time he wants me to write about tantrums and physical restraint. "Wow, that'll be fun," I tell him. So I write the physical restraint story and wait to see what will happen next.

If you can believe it, the author then asks me to write a book. "Are you crazy? Who has the energy to write a friggin' book?" I said. The only page this guy is interested in has two legs and a nice pair of you-know-whats!

But in the end it was an offer I could not refuse. Two

years later, I dotted the last *i* of chapter 10, and here you have it. Now that the book is written, I can see it was worth the effort.

One more thing about me that's important to mention. As you will see in the first chapter, the author has endowed me with quite a brain. I'm able to conceptualize things and use vocabulary light years ahead of my peers. Certainly, having such exceptional intellect is not typical of abused kids living in residential treatment. For that matter, it's not typical of most thirteen-year-olds living anywhere. The reason for having such gifts, I am told, centers on purpose.

Gus E. Studelmeyer, yours truly, was created for the purpose of helping adults, particularly child care professionals, better understand and empathize with abused kids living in residential care. If you're a foster parent or work in a group home, the information should be just as helpful. The author thought that hearing about this stuff from a kid's perspective would make it more interesting and meaningful. And, although my intellect and vocabulary are not typical, I believe the *feelings* I express throughout this book are definitely representative of kids who have been abused.

Speaking of feelings, let me address a somewhat sensitive issue. To truly express my feelings as an abused kid living behind the walls of a residential treatment center, throughout the course of this book I sometimes use rather naughty expletives. Hey, angry, abused kids swear. There ain't no friggin' way around it. (I controlled myself that time.) Hopefully, after an abused kid gets some help he doesn't feel like swearing as much, or he learns some alternative ways to express his anger. It would have been impossible to give an accurate description of life in a residential treatment center without the swearing. I hope some of the words don't offend you. In chapter 4, I get into a pretty weird discussion about feelings and swearing, which should further clarify this issue. Looking back over these chapters, which chronicle two years of my life in a residential treatment center, I see there are a lot more swear words early on. Hey, maybe I'm getting healthier.

For those new to the subject, abused and neglected dudes like me often react to their maltreatment by acting out (i.e., behaving badly). Big surprise. How would you act if you were repeatedly beaten and occasionally got it up the butt? If the acting out in response to abuse and neglect gets too intense, we are often removed from our homes and placed in foster care, group homes, or residential treatment centers. When the big hand of the state first grabs us, attempts are generally made to place us in the "least restrictive environment." I was dropped off at a number of foster homes before my wicked ways finally forced my social worker to throw in the towel and place me in a residential treatment center. I'm told that, ideally, foster and group homes, as well as residential treatment centers, are designed to help a kid and his family stabilize, work on issues, and then reunite. Sometimes it ain't that simple. It wasn't for me, Jack.

Residential treatment centers, and there are lots of them out there, take in the most troubled kids, the ones who act out big time (e.g., hit, kick, bite, steal, tantrum, and piss on the enemy). They are hard places to work in and even harder to live in. Believe me, I know. Looking behind the walls of a residential treatment center, as happens in this book, reveals some very extreme stuff, some incredibly powerful emotions and happenings. So get ready . . . you're in for a ride.

Oh yeah, I almost forgot, the chapters of this book don't necessarily flow one after the other. As stated, it didn't start out to be a book. But there is a progression. And many of the bases, I think, have been covered.

Friends, physical, sexual, and emotional abuse is terrible. Neglect is often worse. There are too many damn kids and adults walking around who have suffered from these things. Enough is enough. This country has to stand up and say, "Cut the shit!" That's what I think. This book is my attempt to make a difference. Although I'm a sharp kid, I don't profess to have all the answers. At the very least, I hope this book gets you thinkin' about this stuff.

I gotta run now. Promised my girlfriend I'd give her a call. Finally got a girlfriend. You see, anything's possible. Remember that.

ONE

WHAT DO I THINK ABOUT RESIDENTIAL TREATMENT

A Youth's Perspective

The following is an essay written by a fictitious thirteen-year-old named Gus Studelmeyer. Gus has been living at a residential center for three years. Inordinately freckled and a wee bit pudgy, Gus possesses an engaging smile—when there is occasion to smile. Lately, he has taken to spiking his red hair (it's orange, if you listen to Gus).

He never knew his father. His mother and her boyfriend (at the time) sexually and physically abused Gus over a period of three years, starting when he was four. After the courts got involved, Gus was placed with his maternal grandparents. He lived with them for two years before excessive tantrumming led to his first foster placement. After "disconnecting" with three successive foster families, Gus was placed at the Highland Hills Treatment Center for Boys, where he currently resides.

I asked Gus if he would write an essay entitled "What Do I Think about Residential Treatment." Here is the document Gus handed me.

Oh, I forgot to mention . . . Gus has an IQ of 163. Gus is a genius.

What Do I Think about Residential Treatment
by Gus E. Studelmeyer

Can you believe the *E* in my name stands for Elvis? Before you go throwing darts at my mom for what she and the asshole did to me, let me explain something. My mom had it pretty tough growing up. She was sexually abused by an uncle who lived in the house, off and on, for seven years. He threatened to kill her if she told. So she didn't until it was too late. In adolescence, drugs and alcohol were not unfamiliar to her. I was a mistake, born three days after her nineteenth birthday. I don't really like talking about this. Suffice it to say, my mom has never been a happy camper. I'm still furious with her for abusing me and watching as that asshole hurt me. But I still love her. She will always be my mom.

After not hearing from or seeing her for over five years, she suddenly appeared one day at the center. Mom actually got her act together and wanted visiting to commence. That really pissed off a lot of the staff at Highland Hills because I was all set to try foster care again. Terribly conflicted about the situation, I took full advantage of the therapeutic milieu to sort through and come to grips with the sudden curve life had so precipitously thrown. I now see my mom every other weekend, on Saturdays from noon to seven. The visits are no longer supervised—and hell, if we aren't talking about an overnight next month. I'm still pretty confused. I still think each visit might be the last one. And I have yet to really express my anger toward her. But Rome wasn't built in a day. Okay, enough about me. Let me tell you about residential treatment.

Your first day is a bitch. You're scared shit. Most kids can vividly recall the details of their first day—the staff who were on duty, the first kids they met, the social worker who brought them, how their room looked. I even remember the first thing I ate: a two-day-old slice of apple pie. Man, did it taste good. I wet the bed my first night. I didn't tell anyone. Some foster parents don't take kindly to boys who leak. But at breakfast my fragrance blew the deception. Margaret, the senior counselor, took me aside and told me that wetting the bed was no big deal. I tried to act cool, but boy was I relieved. (Hey, is that a play on words or what?)

If I were running one of these places, I'd make sure a kid's first day was a good one.

After a while, a few things become very clear about residential treatment. First, it's safe. The staff don't hit the kids, and there are heavy consequences for any kind of violence. This is good. Of course, in the beginning it is the mission of every child to test this out. After all, most of us are unfamiliar with the concept of safety. Some kids "honeymoon" before the testing commences. Not me. I went for the gusto, tantrumming pretty good. I remember one time kicking a staff member named Frank right in the balls. When he didn't strike back, I knew this was my kind of place.

Within a month or two, something else becomes clear

about residential treatment: power permeates the environment. Kids are told what to do, when to do it, and why it should be done. Sure, there's autonomy built in, but the sense of powerlessness can become great. The temptation to misuse power, on the part of staff members, hovers like a fly over shit. Sometimes I think the staff don't understand how powerful they are and how that makes us feel.

Three times I've returned from school to find out my roommate had been changed. "The new combinations make more sense for the group," I get told. Screw you! I hated Billy Parody; Rodney Jones farted all the time; and Carl Spooner was a certified looney. I ask you, the reader, how would you like to drive home one night and find out someone had moved your things across the street and you were now living with Ed Magillicutty? You hate Ed Magillicutty! These kinds of things happen all the time in residential treatment. Most kids have already been subjected to the misuse of power prior to entering a treatment milieu. A lot of anger builds up due to this. Unless staff members are extremely sensitive to this issue, they risk creating and maintaining a sense of alienation between the kids and themselves.

"Why?"

"Because I told you so!"

This kind of power makes me sick. And if we respond angrily to such a power move we get in more trouble. I've always liked the staff members who didn't yell and gave reasons for things. Powerlessness sucks.

On a positive note, it doesn't take long after arriving before you find a new mother. It can be the cook, a counselor, your therapist, or even an older kid. You look for someone who seems special and maybe, just maybe, makes you feel special. Freud called this transference. (I read one of his books in the public library—I had to check out "penis envy" because I thought I had it.)

It seems like all the kids here need to fill the void created by being separated from their moms. What's tough is that people don't stay too long in places like this. Just when you grow attached to someone and feel you can trust them, they leave. This makes it tougher the next time around. I really liked Margaret O'Reilly. No, I *loved* Margaret O'Reilly. When she left, it felt like I was being separated from my mom again. Margaret sent me a card on my birthday; it's still hanging over my bed.

If you work with kids who live away from their homes, you might become pretty important to some of them. I know it's a tough job (just ask Frank, the guy I kicked in the balls), but the longer you hang in, the better we do.

Occasionally, I've seen a staff member get overly attached to a kid. This starts out feeling pretty good to both of them but usually causes a lot of problems. Most of us don't have what you'd consider glowing self-esteem. If we see a staff member favoring a particular kid, it really pisses us off. *"What am I, chopped liver?"* becomes the general sentiment.

Look, I know some of us can be difficult. I was a hellion my first six months, considered quite obnoxious. But it was simply defensive posturing. Kids aren't bad. They're just screwed up. The kid who's pushing you away the most is probably the one who needs you the most.

I think every residential facility would be better off if the staff never used such words as *manipulative, lazy, uninvested, controlling,* and *obnoxious.* They're pejorative adjectives. When you label one of us in such a way, you contaminate the waters, and no one wants to swim with us anymore.

"Manipulative kids aren't fun to work with."

"They're a pain in the ass."

"Boy, is that kid manipulative!"

Every time we get blasted for being "manipulative" (or any other such term), our self-concept suffers. We take on the word. We internalize a sense of badness. Yet the kid you call "manipulative" might have come to your facility with a history of "manipulating" his way out of getting beaten. So maybe manipulating ain't so bad? Maybe it simply needs to be understood in the context of a kid's situation. Maybe people don't need to use these words anymore.

Okay, enough mumbo jumbo, let's talk sex! (You puritans in the audience can pass on the next few paragraphs.)

When you've been sexually abused, it's like your hormone switch gets turned on early. The abuse becomes an unwanted introduction to physical intimacy. In reality, the introduction is more like an invasion—one in which the enemy never leaves. The scars of sexual abuse remain forever (at least that's what my therapist says).

I've really had a hard time with this sex thing. And to be honest, so have the staff. Sometimes it appears that a bomb blast would be more acceptable to them than a blow job in the bathroom. Homosexual experimentation is a real no-no. C'mon, it's not like all of us are championing gay rights. Sexual experimentation is somewhat expectable in a residential treatment environment.

Being a victim of sexual abuse means something bad happened to you that was not in your control—*control* being the operative word here. I guess for some of us who have been dicked, the urge to replicate the sexual aggression, this time from a control position, is rather great. Do *actively* to someone else what was accepted *passively* by you. It's a power thing. It's *mastery*. (I copped a look at some developmental literature, as well.)

We're told sexual feelings are normal, yet God help us if we act on them. It's not like I'm suggesting group orgies be allowed (well, maybe now and then). More sensitivity to biological expression would suffice.

Let's face it, some of us guys are at the perpetual hard-on stage. Some of us lose our minds during this period. Living at a treatment center for boys and not being adequately exposed (and I use the word lightly) to girls is tough. I know the supervisors fear we'll impregnate the local Girl Scout troop if unleashed, but you can't hold back nature.

In reviewing what I've written thus far, it appears I might be painting too negative a picture of residential care. Most of us are angry dudes. When asked to talk about something, our anger often surfaces. We're particularly antiauthority. (Can you blame us?)

It's real hard to admit we like something or someone. We risk disappointment and rejection by committing our affection somewhere. Most of us simply can't tolerate any more rejection. So you see a lot of face-saving and denial to avoid potential pain. A good staff member should be able to see through our "defenses." I love that psychological mumbo jumbo.

I think most kids like the security of residential care more than they let on. Many, like me, are big on moanin' and groanin'.

"This place sucks. You treat us like inmates."

"On my last day, I'm gonna burn this place down"—a particular favorite among the lads.

"How would you *like to live here?"*

"Why don't you staff get a life."

When you think about it, who else can we get mad at? Scream at your mother and there's no visit next week. Swear at your teacher and you get suspended. Tell off your boss and you're history.

We can vent our anger within residential walls and still see daylight. It's wonderful (but don't expect us to admit it). Sometimes a kid will leave the program less angry than when he came in. I think having the opportunity to continually blow off steam helps. It's a necessary evil. Although they often make me nauseous, angry outbursts usually result in "talks" about what is bothering us. I guess some of these "talks" prove beneficial (but don't tell the guys I've admitted this).

Continuing on a positive note, the sports and activities

are great in residential treatment. I did more things in my first six months at Highland Hills than I had done in my entire life. No kiddin'. Some of the sports I had never played before. Most kids are somewhat reluctant to try a sport they're not good at. Self-confidence ain't big among the troops—why risk the embarrassment and pain? But at Highland Hills we have a super activities director, Neil, who understands this. When it came time to play softball, Neil said there would be no striking out, telling us, "It's spring training." (God bless this man!) In August, it was *still* spring training. (You had to love this guy.) People like Neil motivate us to try.

Three years ago I couldn't hit a softball to save my life. Now I plaster the damn thing. When I see that little white circle sailing over the left fielder's head, I feel great. I don't feel like a loser. For kids like me, these are special moments. If it hadn't been for Neil, I'd still be on the sidelines. It's awesome being part of the game.

Most kids in residential care have lousy self-esteem because we blame ourselves for the abuse and neglect we experienced. You have to love your parents, so if they don't treat you right you must be the problem. Residential treatment tries to set the record straight. It attempts to stop us from blaming ourselves for any bad that occurred. The process involves bolstering our self-esteem—giving us new and more positive ways to think about ourselves and life—while helping us come to terms with the reality of our individual situations

You know, after I hit a home run I feel great. I might even

feel good the next day. If I have therapy that day, I might open up more—take a chance. It's funny how the two are connected. I just know it's hard to say certain things when I'm feeling shitty.

Speaking of therapy, what a cushy job. Some kids say they want to become child care workers when they grow up. Not me. I want to be a therapist. Can you imagine getting paid to play and talk with kids? Child care workers have to deal with a lot of crap (remember Frank?). Therapists dress better, probably get paid more, and have the weekends off.

I've read some developmental literature. What a child care worker does is parent two-year-old behavior. Acting out, obstinacy, tantrumming—all normal two-year-old behaviors—occur every day in a residential treatment center. When kids improve and display three-, four-, and five-year-old behavior, they're discharged and a new kid with two-year-old behavior comes in. Like clockwork. Who can parent two-year-old behavior year after year? Is it really such a mystery why child care workers don't last too long? It's a brutal job. No thank you, this guy is going to be a therapist.

[Note to my friends living in out of-home placements: I'm not saying we're two-year-olds. We're cool. Very cool. But some of us didn't get it very good when we were one, two, and three. So we are still looking for (needing) the same kind of love and attention we required then. It's like a hole in us that needs to be filled.]

Okay, back to therapy . . . Look, I know I exaggerate the finer points of the profession. Some kids and parents would be pretty tough to meet with on a regular basis. Actually, I vaguely recall annihilating my first therapist's office. But he was a jerk and deserved the trashing. He forced me to talk about things *I didn't want to talk about!* Shit. I still get mad when I think about him.

My second therapist, Ellen, has her act together. We play a lot of pool and card games. She isn't too aggressive on the talk front. But hell, if we don't do some great work together. I'm still not sure how she extracts it out of me.

But even though I like her I don't always want to meet. She's cool about this. At times I get pissed off because she's pretty tight with the residential staff. If she has a safety concern regarding something I've said, right to the child care staff she goes. I guess on some level I appreciate this, but in general it pisses me off.

Some of the other therapists in the building are know-it-alls. They clearly look down on the child care workers. Big mistake. If a kid can get a good rift going between his therapist and the child care staff, it's worth a lot of points (i.e., extra attention). There's nothing we enjoy more than good old-fashioned "splitting." It's no fun when we are the only ones upset.

Most kids in residential care are experts in the art of provocation—plainly speaking, getting people pissed off. Staff members are sometimes hard to crack, but fellow inmates (kids) are easy. Contrary to public opinion, there is real purpose behind peer antagonism. For one thing, we're terrified of being "crazy." We've been poked and prodded by shrinks; analyzed, evaluated, assessed, tested, shmested . . . Catch my drift, reader? Ending up in a residential treatment center for *emotionally disturbed youth* does little to assuage our fears of insanity. So, how does a kid (like me) test the waters to prove he hasn't gone off the deep end? It's not that difficult. Peer antagonism can do the trick.

For example, Bruce goes wild when you call his mother a dyke. Say it and I guarantee he'll be tantrumming in five minutes. The kid is out to lunch. And when Bruce is going wild, all the other kids sit back and feel good. Why? Because we're not as bonkers as Bruce. He becomes the yardstick. As long as we don't act worse than Bruce, we're not crazy. *Bruce* is crazy. At times we're all pretty good to him. We need Bruce.

Sometimes I wonder what ordinary kids dream about. What did Wally and the Beaver imagine each night? Me, I dream about being an ordinary kid.

"Ward, will you tell the boys to come down for dinner?"

"I'll be happy to, dear."

(Ward walks to the bottom of the stairs and looks up.) *"Boys, time for dinner. Wally, Beaver, Gus, c'mon down before it gets cold."*

Wally, Beaver, and Gus. Boy, does that sound goooood! I'm pretty jealous of ordinary kids like the Beave. I don't think they understand how wonderful they have it. Sometimes ordinary kids make fun of us residential dwellers. That really sucks. Let's trade places for a day!

Now and then I get nervous about telling an ordinary

kid where I live. You never know how they'll react. I once decked a kid for making fun of Highland Hills. (Actually, he beat the crap out of me. I was taking poetic license.)

I've got to stop now—we're going roller skating in a few minutes. That means babes!

Look, if you happen to come across a pudgy, redheaded adolescent with a few zits who lives in a residential treatment center but still looks like Tom Cruise, give him a break. He deserves it. He's trying. No shit.

TWO

THE RESTRAINT

For this chapter I've been asked to wear a wire. Yeah, like in the cop movies. The author wants to intersperse throughout my personal reflections actual dialogue that typically occurs in a group home or residential treatment center. Sounds like an interesting concept.

It's been a number of months since I finished writing the first chapter. During this past year, my mother got her act back together and visiting commenced, for the first time in five years. After eight months of seeing her, a decision was finally made for me to return home. In fact, I'm going on a home visit in twenty minutes. My mother canceled our last visit because of car problems.

Tape recorder on.

It's now 10:10 a.m. She's ten minutes late. Usually, she calls when she's going to be late. I hate when she's late. There's a car pulling in now. It could be her. Damn, it's Wayne, the maintenance man. It's now 10:20 a.m. She's really late.

"Where the heck is she?"

Maybe she's not coming. That would be two missed visits in a row. The bitch is losing it again—I just know it. Where the hell is she?

"Maybe it's me?"

I always drove her crazy. Hell, I probably made her drink. 10:22 a.m. 10:23 a.m. 10:25 a.m.

If she comes in the next ten minutes, I won't get mad at her. I can't get mad at her. I don't want to blow it. Please, God, don't let me blow it.

"Gus."

"Yeah."

"Before you go, could you please straighten up your room? It's a mess. I asked you nicely to take care of it an hour ago."

"Chris, my mother's coming in a second. I'll clean it when I get back."

"Gus, you know the rule: rooms need to be cleaned before visits. C'mon I'll give you a hand."

"I'm not doing it now. I told you, Chris, I'll clean it when I get back."

"Look, I know you're a little nervous about your mom being late, but the room has to be done now."

"Fuck you, asshole. I'm gonna stand here and wait for my mother. If you get near me, I'll knock the shit out of you."

"Gus, could you please go sit on your bed for a while?"

"Make me and this is what I'll do to you!"

"John, could you come over here? Gus just put his hand through the dry wall. We need to bring him to the Quiet Room."

"Get the fuck away from me. Don't touch me!"

"Can you walk with us?"

"Fuck you! Get away from me! Ah . . . shit . . . fuck you . . . let go of my arms! You're hurting me . . . Let me goooo!"

"Okay, let's put him on the floor."

"Get off of me!

"Take it easy, Gus."

"Get off me, assholes . . . what are you trying to do, hump me? Fuckin' homos . . . get off me . . . you're breaking my arms . . . Jesus, don't hold me so hard . . . I can't breathe!"

"You're okay, Gus. Take it easy."

"Get off. You're hurting me. Get off me! I'll kill both of you when I get up. Help!"

"John, hold his head. He's starting to bang it."

"Let go of my head! Let go! Ma, they're killing me! Let go! I can't breathe!"

"Are you going to bang it anymore?"

"No, let go."

"Okay, John, take your hands off his head."

"Assholes . . . I . . . hate it here! I'll sue all you bastards! Let me go! Child abuse! They're hurting me! Help! Anybody!"

"Take it easy, Gus."

"Get off!"

"That's it. Just relax. Take a breath. Don't worry, it's okay. I'm going to let your arms go. Good. All right, I'm getting off you now. Why don't you lie here for a few more minutes. That's it."

"She didn't come, did she?"

"No, she didn't, and that stinks."

"Can I go sit on my bed?"

"Sure."

Tape recorder off.

Maybe this tape recording deal ain't such a great thing. Pretty intense, eh? Jesus, I haven't been physically restrained in over a year. I know it's a necessary evil, but boy does it suck. You lie helplessly on your stomach with your hands held at your sides. The adults on top of you straddle your legs and secure your arms. The more you struggle, the harder the "restrainer" pushes down. When this occurs, it sometimes gets hard to breathe (or at least it feels that way). You scream, you swear, you desperately try to scratch the restrainer's hands.

Sometimes you lose it. You forget where you are. You forget who's holding you. Sometimes the person holding you becomes the guy who raped or abused you. The swears, the taunts, the striking out. Some of this, of course, is pure, unadulterated rage. But I also think it's intended to provoke the restrainers into actually hurting us. If we can get a youth care worker to hurt us, the incident helps solidify our poor self-images. New abuse reinforces the feelings that developed in response to the old abuse.

I think all kids in residential care have lousy self-esteem, because on some level they need to believe the abuse they experienced was deserved. We grow to believe we were abused because we were (and are) bad. After all, a kid can't figure out that abuse at the hands of a parent is the parent's mistake. Kids have to love their parents . . . stick up for them . . . be loyal. Who else is there for us? It's simple, Jack.

Residential treatment tries to give us a different perspective. We learn that any kind of abuse is wrong but the people who did it are not necessarily bad—they just did bad things, made horrible choices, and need help. It's a hard pill to swallow, and some of us never quite digest it.

I hate to admit it, but I think some of us try to get restrained because we want to be held. We're maybe feeling out of control, unloved, lonely, and ashamed of who we are and what happened to us. Being held firmly can be quite comforting. There probably would be fewer restraints in residential care if there were more hugs.

Every kid needs attention. Kids who have suffered abuse need even more but don't always know how to ask for it. A lot of us don't think we deserve it or that anybody would want to give it to us. Hopefully, a kid will learn to "appropriately" seek attention in residential care and to feel good about himself. But when all else fails, a hand through the wall will get two hands around the body.

Some staff members are pretty quick to restrain a kid. I think it has to do with control. We all want to be in control. When we lose control, we get anxious. For most kids in residential care, bad things happened to them because they lacked control, were helpless while being abused. Staff members also want control, but each seems to have a different threshold for losing it.

Look, I know it is not always easy to decide when to physically intervene with a kid, but it's a pretty damn serious type of intervention. Kids and staff members can both get hurt during restraints. And kids, like this dude, are at risk of reliving the trauma we suffered while being held so forcefully. If I ran one of these places, I'd train my staff up the wazoo in principles and strategies to *avoid* restraints. And I'd look under every rock for the best way to do it. Man, getting on top of us, with our arms clasped at our sides, can't be the best way to hold us. That's got to change. I have to believe they will develop better methods for doing this—and clarify the reasons for physical intervention in the first place.

Now, of course, there are ways of getting back at those staff members who seem to delight in prematurely grabbing us. We once had a child care worker named Rudy, an asshole with a short fuse who would put you on the floor if you just looked at him the wrong way. He'd hold you hard, and he'd hurt you—not enough to get him reported, just enough to make your eyes water and your mouth spit. Before the agency canned the bastard (there was a rumor that he was put on probation), we exacted our revenge.

When Rudy was starting to really piss us off, one of us got the idea to employ Bruce. Squeamish readers might want to skip the next few paragraphs—they're slightly indelicate. The goal was to get Rudy out. The plan was ingenious, conceived after tuck-in one hot, steamy night, with the aid of contraband devil dogs and Dr. Pepper. It involved Bruce and it was messy. We loved it. To make a long story short, we each paid Bruce a buck if every time he had to take a crap he would get restrained by Rudy. The plan was beautiful in its simplicity. Although the house stunk for two weeks, Rudy soon vanished. We hated Rudy. We loved Brucie. We needed Brucie. I guess it's not very nice that we took advantage of him.

Most kids in residential care really need to look out for number one since no one else has. If exploiting another kid so we don't feel too crazy, or enacting revenge against a lousy staff member, does the trick, we do it. It's not something I'm really proud of. It's probably time for me to make better choices when I'm questioning myself or angry at a staff member.

But our plan to terminate Rudy worked. I guess we have more control than we think.

Tape recorder on.

"Gus, you doing okay?"

"Yeah, Chris. I'm all right."

"Can we talk?"

"Who are you, Dr. Phil?"

"Glad you haven't lost your sense of humor."

"Never."

"Hey, that was a tough scene. You were pretty upset."

"My damn mother. Two visits in a row she's missed, without a call."

"That's pretty lousy. You feel like something's going on?"

"I'm feeling like it's falling apart. She's slipping back."

"What were the last few visits like? You didn't talk much about them."

"Not so great. She seemed more on edge, more nervous. I think she's having trouble at work, and I found some Southern Comfort under the sofa."

"Doesn't sound too good."

"It sucks. I'm scared and I'm pissed."

"Who can blame you? It's too bad we couldn't have talked like this before the fireworks."

"It was building up inside me. I just couldn't handle what was going on. Guess I'll be working to pay off that hole in the wall?"

"Yup, you're in debt, man. Gus, you were really upset. We had to hold you pretty good. Are you okay about what went on?"

"Sure, I understand how things work."

"You know, we don't like having to hold kids like that. In fact, we've got a big training coming up. I think we're going to learn some better ways to prevent physical interventions and do the holds only if necessary."

"That's good to hear. And long overdue!"

"Yeah, I agree. 'Cause what we're doing now ain't fun for anyone."

"It was for Rudy."

"Until you paid Bruce."

"You knew about that?"

"Rudy was in the wrong business, and Bruce would have done it for nothing. You guys should lay off of Bruce."

"Damn, you guys know everything!"

"Not everything. We still haven't figured out who snuck in the devil dogs."

"Seriously, Chris, I know you care, and I appreciate the way you talk with me. You're a good guy."

"Thanks, Gus. We're tryin'."

Tape recorder off.

When I was approached about wearing a wire, I never thought you'd be hearing voices from the floor. But what the hell, residential treatment ain't always pretty. Physical restraint happens, probably more than it should. It's a damn serious intervention.

When I first came to Highland Hills, I often lost control and needed to be held. But other kids have come to the center with less anger and more control. Those kids don't need physical interventions. But some of them get it anyways because they follow the crowd. They jump on the bandwagon: *Friends, if you're feeling lonely, angry, or just plain shitty don't hold it in. Don't wait to talk to someone. No, friends, the answer is: Get restrained. For only a temporary consequence you, too, can be thrust on the floor and held like a bloomin' idiot. You'll get attention, notoriety, and the physical intimacy you so desperately crave. It's like a drug! It feels good! Buy it!*

It really shouldn't be this way. Troubled kids should be put with normal kids so they don't learn more bad habits, like getting restrained when you don't need to be.

Look, if you happen to work with kids in foster care or a residential treatment center, remember we weren't born bad. If you have to touch us, a hug feels pretty good, but the floor is often cold. You owe it to us to know what you are doing.

You've got a really hard job; I'd never do it. Sometimes I think about becoming a therapist, but that ain't easy either. Executive Director Gus E. Studelmeyer—now that sounds pretty good.

"Director Studelmeyer?"

"Yes?"

"Some of the boys were caught eating devil dogs after tuck-in last night."

"What do you think we should do?"

"What we should have done a long time ago."

"What's that?"

"Fire Rudy . . . and break out the Pepper!"

THREE
FOSTER CARE

After my mom canceled a slew of home visits and a number of appointments with my therapist, the writing on the wall gradually turned to graffiti. I saw it coming. I'm not sure I wanted it to work. Too much history. It's not like I had a choice. But she was, and is, my mother. I gave it my best shot, and maybe she did, too. Now it's foster care, again—or prepare for independent living. Life sucks.

I guess my mom just wasn't cut out for the maternal thing. I have to accept that (I'm told). Yet I have so many mixed feelings. At times rage dominates, while on other occasions loneliness and despair flood the old cerebrum.

Maybe when I'm eighteen and have my act together, we'll reunite. I've seen a lot of kids leave this place over the years. Sooner or later, they all seem to end up back home, no matter how bad it was—or is. Blood is thicker than crap, I guess.

Intellectually, I can grasp the concept that I must rise above the rubble of my past, but to do so I will need fuel, sustenance, hope. And where does someone like me find such energy? Why the hell should I, or any kid in my situation—and there are lots of us dudes—be hopeful? Remember, I've already blown out of three foster homes, and before that I was abused at home.

Being hopeful implies we expect something good to happen. When you've been bounced around and abused, you don't expect good to happen, because good only happens to "good" people. The "other" people. Not us.

My life has been one long series of disconnections. Like a car getting gas, if the nozzle never stays in long enough (keeps getting jerked) you don't go very far—unless, of course, you come upon a new station in life that supplies the fuel without interruption. Those of us who end up in foster care or residential treatment need to have the right kind of people battling for and with us, folks who constantly try to fill our tanks even in the face of treacherous fireworks.

Such people need to truly understand who we are and where we are coming from. (Hint: It ain't the wonderful Land of Oz.) This kind of information enables helpers to form reasonable expectations concerning our behavior and personalities—and to stick by us when the going gets rough.

The road is damn hard. Each new station begins to look like the one that caused your original engine trouble. The tendency is to pull out before someone starts jerkin' the nozzle again. You keep leavin' with that empty feeling, but at least you pay a little less. I think "emptiness" is quite pervasive among the troops.

Such is the life of a damaged child. We are all empty and require lots of filling, but when the filling starts we often panic and attempt to sabotage the fuel intake. Having it precipitously shut off again brings the worst kind of pain. Better to sabotage and end things yourself than have the fuel stop without warning. Ellen, my therapist, has a sign posted in her office that reads: "Hope is Humanity's Fuel." I'm chuggin' along on fumes, brother.

I've seen a lot of kids blow out of foster care because the foster parents overreacted to the kids' behavior. Some had no clue what those kids were about; they weren't properly informed. I think foster parents get a bad rap. The problem is in the training and support, or lack thereof. But then, you can't go blaming the state Social Service Departments, the people in charge of overseeing foster parents, because they'll just cry poverty. I face this firsthand when my yearly clothing allowance gets cut.

Then who do you blame? I don't know. Maybe it's capitalism and the almighty need to make a buck. There just don't seem to be enough people in this country who give a damn about their fellow man. Folks seems to focus more on their wallets than on the kid next door who is always sad and crying. So, is there no hope for me and my comrades? Does the path leading from abuse and neglect go only in one direction—south? Hell, no! But to rise above the muck takes hard work and luck.

Wow, I'm all screwed up and freaked just thinking about foster care. I can't believe I'll be going through it again. I've been through foster care before. It's a real crapshoot. Please, God, find me a great family. Man, I'm really getting tired.

It's a few minutes before bedtime, and I need some zzzs. I'll try to . . . (yawn) . . . write a few more lines. Gotta put some jokes in . . . (yawn) . . . seems too serious . . . I'm sleepy.

"Gus."

"Yes, Director Pittslotti."

Director Pittslotti: I'd like you to meet your new foster parents, Jill and Orville Brady.

Gus: The Bradys, no shit! What, Brad and Angelina couldn't take in another kid?

Jill: We're so happy to finally meet you, Gus. Here, would you like some chocolate chip cookies? I baked them myself.

Gus: Are they real chocolate chips or carob?

Jill: Chocolate chips.

Gus: Good. The cook here turned holistic last year. I'm sick of her "natural" crapola. Mmm, these are great!

Orv: Gus, we've got a room all set up for you with a TV, Xbox, CD player, iPod, iPad, and Nintendo. We hope you'll like joining our family.

Gus: I'm warming up to the idea.

Director Pittslotti: Gus, the Bradys have no other children and recently won the grand prize in the state's lottery.

Gus: Getting hot, very hot.

Jill: Gus, do you have any questions for us?

Gus: Yeah, one, the big one. Are you two gonna dump me like all the other foster parents did?

Orv: Gus, we'll never give up on you. Never.

Gus: But what if I act up big time? Steal your car, French kiss your grandmother, eat Jell-O with my hands?

Jill: (smiling) We expect you to test us, to see if we'll be like all the others.

Orv: We know if it starts feeling good in our household you'll probably panic . . .

Jill: And try to sabotage the placement before we end it. Isn't that the typical pattern?

Orv: I guess it all comes down to expectations.

Jill: And we know what to expect.

Orv: We know there will be hard times.

Jill: And we know that talk is cheap. Words mean little. Trust is earned.

Orv: We'll need to practice what we preach, and we shall.

Jill: Bet on it.

Gus: Sounds good. But what if you die?

Orv: We won't die, Gus.

Gus: You won't die?

Orv: Director Pittslotti, tell him.

Director Pittslotti: Gus, Jill and Orville are the best foster parents in the world. Just like in the old *Newlywed Game,* they are a "gift" (family) chosen just for you. Nothing can go wrong. No disruptions, no deaths.

Gus: Wow, this is hard to believe. I've never had a break in my life. This can't be happening.

Director Pittslotti: It's real, Gus. They will be with you for as long as you need them.

Gus: I've been sexually abused. My whole orientation to intimacy has been skewed. My previous foster parents freaked when the sexual acting out commenced—even the best ones. You ready for that?

Jill: Gus, my cousin is Dr. Drew. He's great with the sex stuff.

Orv: And in the sixties I was an active nudist. We have traveled the many roads of human sexuality. We are both comfortable about handling your driving.

Gus: Oh, I like the way you put that. A little play on Freud. Nice touch.

Orv: Thank you. Gus, we won't reject you, even if you kick me in the balls.

Gus: Guess you read about poor Frank. I still feel bad about that. And what about my mother?

Jill: Your mom will always be welcome in our household, and you can visit her as you see fit.

Orv: We're not going to compete with your mother. That would be wrong. We're all on the same team. The "Gus team."

Gus: Yo team!

Jill: If it feels right for the two of you to be re united, we'll do everything we can to make that a reality.

Orv: She's your mother, and she'll always be your mother.

Gus: Hey, I've written that before.

Jill: We know. We've enjoyed your articles.

Gus: Can I go to college?

Jill: We've secured a scholarship to Harvard for you. But where you go will, of course, be your choice.

Gus: Fuckin' A!

Orv: We prefer you not swear. It gets kids in trouble.

Gus: So, you'll give me consequences when I act devilish?

Jill: Sure.

Orv: We'll also explain why every consequence is given, and if possible, we'll let you be part of deciding the correct form of discipline.

Gus: What if I become physically aggressive toward one or both of you?

Jill: We, like Superman, are from the planet Krypton. We can't be hurt.

Gus: You are now yankin' my chain. You expect me to believe you both have superpowers? Please . . .

Orv: Gus, with my X-ray vision I can see the contents

of your pocket. In it you have three dollars and forty-three cents.

Jill: And a Manny Ramirez baseball card.

Orv: And one slightly used cond——

Gus: Okay, you've made your point, I believe. But what about Kryptonite?

Orv: We've developed an immunity to it.

Gus: Gosh. You guys are everything a kid could want in foster parents.

Director Pittslotti: Gus, they're the best!

Gus: But what about my pain?

Jill: You mean inside?

Gus: Yeah. Will you—can you—make it go away? X-ray it to the phantom zone?

Orv: Do you want it to go away? Do you want me to ease all of your bad memories?

Jill: Would you like a fresh start?

Gus: You can do that?

Orv and Jill: Gus, we're the best, remember?

Director Pittslotti: Would you like a fresh start, Gus? Would you like the Bradys to implant a different set of memories?

Gus: Hmm, let me think about that. Could I have another cookie while I'm thinkin'?

Jill: Sure, we made them just for you, Gus.

Director Pittslotti: Well, do you want your slate cleaned?

Gus: No, I don't think so. As terrible as I've had it, that would be like giving up. Part of me thinks I can work through the muck. I'm not a quitter. But sometimes the pain gets real bad and I feel like such a loser. As if I brought it all on myself. I know I should try to release it, but I feel so ashamed of myself for letting it happen. Shame is a real crippler.

Orv: We know that, Gus. Most kids in your situation feel that way.

Jill: When the pain gets bad, we'll be with you. You've got nothing to be ashamed of. Nothing that happened was your fault. You're our hero.

Orv: And we'll always be with you.

Gus: What if my acne never clears and I get fatter?

Jill: Our X-ray vision will cure your acne.

Orv: And if you get fatter there will just be more of you to love.

Gus: You guys are unreal!

Director Pittslotti: They're the best!

Gus: Can my friends at Highland Hills come and visit, as well as some of the child care workers?

Orv: Of course.

Gus: Can my roommate, Hector, do sleepovers?

Jill: Absolutely, if it's okay with Mr. Pittslotti and Hector's mother.

Gus: Will I get an allowance?

Orv: Ten dollars a week.

Jill: If you do your chores.

Gus: Can I smoke cigarettes?

Orv: Do you really want to smoke?

Gus: Damn right, I do.

Jill: Even if you'll die of lung cancer at the early age of forty-three?

Orv: After two operations and ten painful months of chemotherapy?

Gus: What . . . you can read the future?

Orv and Jill: Gus, we're the . . .

Gus: Best . . . I remember. Okay, to hell with the smoking. I will choose not to smoke.

Orv: Good decision.

Gus: When do you guys plan to take me? Will I have time to "terminate," as they say?

Jill: We know how important it is to say good-bye.

Orv: You can't say hello . . .

Jill: Until you say good-bye.

Gus: Hey, you've got that down pretty good.

Orv: We practice a lot, remember . . .

Gus: You're the best.

Director Pittslotti: Well, Gus, what do you think?

Gus: I think Lady Luck has finally flown my way. This sounds almost too good to believe. Let's go for it.

Orv and Jill: Great!

Gus: One last question.

Jill: Yes.

Gus: Will I have to clean my room?

Orv: Only if you want to. We have a maid who has been with us a long time.

Gus: Let me guess—her name's Alice, right?

Jill: Why, yes, how did you know?

Gus: Just lucky, I guess.

"Gus, Gus, wake up. You fell asleep at the desk. Gus, I think you were dreaming."

"What . . . Where am I? Hector, is that you?"

Hector: No, it's Bart Simpson. Who the hell do you think it is?

Gus: Hector. I'm getting out of here. The Bradys and Alice are going to be my new foster family. They said you can do overnights!

Hector: Gus, wake up, man, you were dreaming. This is Highland Hills, and you ain't goin' nowhere.

Gus: It wasn't a dream. I'm going. And don't use those double negatives anymore. What are you going to do without me?

Hector: Gus, you're thirteen years old. You live at Highland Hills. Your mother just blew you off. Now, you've got to hope for something new—like a goddamn miracle. Because most foster parents want young and attractive. Pimples, fat, adolescent, that's not what most people are looking for. You know that.

Gus: Shit! It was such a great dream. They were the best.

Hector: The Bradys. The Bradys! After Marsha, what was there?

Gus: They were really cool about me having contact with my mother.

Hector: Sure, and I suppose they were gonna send you to Yale?

Gus: No, Harvard. And they would never reject me. And beat this, they would never die.

Hector: Gus, wake up. This is the real world—it ain't make-believe.

Gus: I love make-believe.

Hector: Yeah, because it's fantasy. But we live in a pukey reality.

Gus: God, it sucks waking up.

The preceding dialogue between Hector and yours truly, as well as the dream sequence, was transcribed from memory. Hey, that was one helluva dream. I would have enjoyed meeting Alice. She seemed like such a hot ticket. And having my pimples obliterated by X-ray vision— man, we're talkin' teenage heaven.

Boy, you don't have to be a shrink to figure out where I'm coming from. I'm scared shit about my future. I've read that in adolescence we're supposed to be "separating," forging a new identity. How the hell can I, or kids like me, get on with life when our past is so unresolved? You can't jump off a diving board if there's a crack in it. Well, I've got cracks—actually, crevices.

Sure, there are some great foster parents out there, heroic individuals who devote their lives to helping kids like me, but not enough get the kind of training and support they really need to optimally care for troubled kids. Most of the staff at Highland Hills tell me it takes about a year of comprehensive training and hands-on experience to become a competent youth care worker. Yet, from what I see and hear, foster parents are asked to parent kids full-time with much less training and often with marginal support because their poor caseworkers are often overloaded.

It really doesn't make sense. It's not like we're "cured" when someone designates us ready for foster care. Life will always be tough. The emotional work never ends for victims of abuse—bet on that, Jack. We need the right people ready and willing to bring us into their homes when we leave residential care.

My therapist would be proud of me for expressing my feelings so articulately. (Actually, she is proud of me—I copped a look at her progress notes. It didn't take a genius to sneak into her office, although if it did I'd still have gotten in.

In spite of my venting, there are definitely foster care success stories, and I'm not giving up hope that I'll be one of them. I've got some good people at Highland Hills who believe in me. They supply the fuel, and I'm getting filled. But every now and then it feels like I'm playing the game of life against a stacked deck. Every day that goes by without a change, in my case, hurts.

It doesn't have to be this way. Maybe when I'm older I'll try to do something about the foster care problem—find a way to train and pay them accordingly. But right now I'm more interested in getting some booty and having a good time. Jesus, I'm going to be fourteen in five months. I've got some experimenting to do. I've got to rise above the rubble and do some living.

FOUR

FEELINGS

I think most kids who have suffered abuse have an inexorable fascination with the dark side, the supernatural, and the unknown. We tend to attribute the cause of our misery to these forces. It would be too simple, and too damn painful, to blame our parents for the emotional havoc they inflicted or contributed to. And although most of us hurtin' dudes tend to blame ourselves for all the bull that has occurred we're always looking for an "out"—something or someone else to blame. That's where the dark side comes in.

Many troubled children believe they have the devil lurking inside of them.

"I got beaten because of the devil inside of me."

"The devil makes me do bad things."

"I think the devil is inside my mother, too."

Actually, this is a nice way of getting people off the hook. All blame falls on the devil (and he couldn't care less).

Horror stories can be another kind of "out." I just finished reading Stephen King's *Four Past Midnight*, a collection of four pulsating stories that disrupt your emotional rhythm.

Horror writers like King are popular among the troops. We've had such horrific things done to us that it is kind of therapeutic to read about someone else getting terrorized or going nuts. The King-man lets us control the terror—maybe for the first time. We buy the books (if we choose). We read them (at our discretion). And we finish them unscathed (at times). It's beautiful. That's why we also love the slasher movies.

The second story in this King collection, "Secret Window, Secret Garden," involves a popular fiction writer who is confronted by an unsettling stranger accusing the writer of plagiarizing one of his stories. Is the stranger real or a figment of the writer's imagination? Legitimate dude or alter ego? King, of course, keeps us in suspense until the very end, as he weaves a chilling tale of baleful delight.

Well, buckos, King's story got me thinking—and irritated. Who is this guy who created me? What's his angle? Being a fictitious character, I have no rights, no privileges, no control. When the writer wants me to say or do something, I comply. (Give me your paw, Gus. Thatta boy!) I'm continually being turned inside out. Readers have already been allowed a penetrating look into my psyche. You read about my history; you were there when I tantrummed and got restrained; you experienced my tears; and in the last chapter, I exposed my fear and ambivalence about foster care.

So I have been wondering, are the opinions that flow from my mouth mine or those of the guy who created me? How come I get turned inside out in every chapter and he walks away smelling like a rose (and then gets all the credit)? Is he hiding behind me? Even a fictitious character wants his own identity. I want to know where the author ends and Gus begins. I want some boundaries, man. I won't be used. I don't care if the author has me commit suicide in the next chapter or step in dog shit, it's time for a confrontation.

"Hey, you with the moustache and Brillo-pad head. I want to talk to you."

"My name is Charlie—you know that."

"Yes, of course I know that. In fact, your full name is Charles D. Appleberg."

"Don't get wise. It's Appelstein."

> Gus: Excuse me, I'm upset.
>
> Charlie: You know I shouldn't be talking to you like this.
>
> Gus: Why not?
>
> Charlie: Because you're fictitious. You don't exist. I made you up.
>
> Gus: Fuck you. That's a cop out.
>
> Charlie: You don't have to swear. I get criticized about your language. Why don't you tone it down?
>
> Gus: Fuck you.
>
> Charlie: Cut it out.
>
> Gus: I'll cut it out if you promise to stick around and talk.
>
> Charlie: Okay, but this is ridiculous. I'll be talking to myself.

Gus: Will you? That's exactly what I want to find out.

Charlie: What do you mean?

Gus: I mean . . . how much of me is you?

Charlie: I'm all you. You don't exist.

Gus: You're not catching my drift, Chuck.

Charlie: Don't call me Chuck. I hate that name.

Gus: Let me explain the situation. In the first chapter, for instance, you have me decree that I hate it when people misuse power.

"Why?"

"Because I told you so."

Remember—

Charlie: Of course I remember. I wrote those lines.

Gus: Well then, do I, your noble representative of residential treatment, really hate the misuse of power? Or is the opinion overstated and maybe more representative of your own issues around authority and power? Did someone diddle you along the way?

Charlie: Stupid questions. *The Gus Chronicles I* isn't about me. It's about you and who you typify.

Gus: Bullshit! Are you stating that you or anyone else can write passionately and objectively about kids like me, their families, and their stays in out-of-home placements? That you can do this without your own feelings and history getting in the way? That's bull; you know better.

Charlie: What's your point?

Gus: My point, your Heinass, is obvious. It's fuckin' easy . . .

Charlie: Hey!

Gus: It's friggin' easy to do what you're doing—to create a character, me, and chapter after chapter pull his strings without acknowledging or taking any responsibility for how your own issues and feelings might be influencing his words and actions.

Charlie: Readers don't want to know and certainly don't care about my personal issues and motivations. They're immaterial. Since when are fiction writers required to bare their souls? Does Stephen King tell you how it feels to write each story and why?

Gus: Knock knock. Hello in there.

Charlie: Hey, don't touch me!

Gus: Touch you? I can't. I'm fictitious, remember? Feeling on edge, Chuck?

Charlie: Please do not call me Chuck. It bugs me.

Gus: Sorry, I tend to get provocative when I'm hungry. Do you think we could call a temporary truce and order some Domino's pizza?

Charlie: You can't be hungry—you have no stomach. I'm not calling Domino's.

Gus: Okay, fine, I'm not real—but I'm still hungry. So go to your keyboard and type me up a

big juicy steak, smother it in gravy, and
throw me a side of fried peppers and onions.

Charlie: Okay, no problem. One big juicy steak
coming right up.

Gus was famished. He ordered a big juicy steak, and the
waiter dutifully brought it out. Gus feverishly severed the first
succulent piece and triumphantly brought it to his mouth.
Tears of joy began to roll down his face. He would chew it
slowly, he would remember this moment. "Shit, what the
fuck!" Like a volcanic eruption, the contents of Gus's mouth
violently discharged onto his unsuspecting lap. "It's liver! I
hate fuckin' liver!"

Charlie: (laughing) Sometimes I just amaze myself.

Gus: Was that your idea of a joke, Chuck?

Charlie: I told you not to call me Chuck. Keep it up
and I'll have you snorting sushi.

Gus: Okay, let's get back to the issue at hand.

Charlie: Good idea.

Gus: Feelings, man, that's what I'm talking about.
Nothing more than feelings.

Charlie: I used to love that song.

Gus: Never heard of it. You're old.

Charlie: But good-lookin'.

Gus: Check your glasses—it's time for thicker
frames.

Charlie: Your point?

Gus: You dudes who work with kids, or teach others how to do it, can't pretend you don't have feelings, the kind that get in the way.

Charlie: Yeah, so . . .

Gus: So! If a youth care worker comes in after having a fight with his babe, we kids suffer. And if we complain about his mood, he denies it and probably gets angrier.

Charlie: It could happen.

Gus: And if a foster mother had a hurtin' childhood, it sometimes will play out in how she deals with us. There's that risk.

Charlie: So what are you trying to say?

Gus: It's brutal working with troubling boys like me. We push your buttons. We get under your skin. That's our mission—to see if you'll screw us over like the people who initially did. We're trying to make sense of the world. We've got big questions that only you can answer. Can adults be trusted? Am I good or bad? Etc.

Charlie: And if we don't have our acts together, can't look inside, or some of our unwanted baggage slips through the door, the answers might come out wrong.

Gus: Bingo, brother.

Charlie: Therapists sometimes refer to this as "countertransference."

Gus: Jack, I don't care what they call it. I only care

about people in youth care recognizing it. It pisses me off when staff members poke and prod my feelings while denying their own. I've seen some pretty good workers appear to wilt under the heat because they couldn't show some vulnerability, or get in touch with who they are and where they're coming from.

Charlie: Are you pointing a finger at me?

Gus: Yeah, the middle one.

Charlie: Why?

Gus: Because you haven't had the guts to examine how much of me is really you. Not all kids in out-of-home placements talk and act like me. Where are you taking poetic license and why? What's inside of you that makes me tick? C'mon, dude, model some honesty and vulnerability if you want folks in this field to pay more attention to . . . counter-transference.

Charlie: Sure you don't want pizza?

Gus: I'm waiting.

Charlie: How about if I find you a female friend in the next chapter?

Gus: Still waiting.

Charlie: Okay, I'll talk. But it won't be easy.

Gus: This stuff ain't ever easy.

Charlie: Well, first of all, I really do believe you are, in fact, quite representative of kids in foster care and residential treatment.

Gus: Still waiting—now startin' to feel like that damn little bunny in the Eveready commercials.

Charlie: All right. Not every kid would write about this stuff and use as many swear words as you do.

Gus: Hmm, that's interesting. So where are my swears coming from?

Charlie: Okay, I swear a bit too much. My father had a wicked temper, and I learned some good ones from him. Although kids in out-of-home placements tend to swear a lot, maybe I've taken extra license with you. Maybe I've let some of my own baggage seep out through you?

Gus: Nice admission, big guy. Maybe you should do some more soul-searching before you write any more.

Charlie: Giving you a proclivity toward the four-letter word—even though it might have something to do with the way I was raised, hasn't detracted from getting your message across. When I write about and work with at-risk kids, I am constantly assessing my feelings and thinking about factors that might be influencing my actions (like a dad with a bad temper). If I blow an interaction due to some unresolved baggage or inappropriate feelings, I have to take responsibility, apologize, and try to learn from the mistake. If I, or anyone else, blows too many interactions due to undetected baggage getting through, it's time for a change or professional assistance. Psychotherapists and others engaged in emotional helping professions are often encouraged to be in therapy themselves. There shouldn't be a stigma associated with this. Working day to day with people who are hurting can, and often does, bring out the hurt in ourselves. Sometimes adults who have been traumatized as children choose to work in places like this to help resolve the difficult feelings with which they still struggle. But to be truly effective one has to be aware of this reality and not let the baggage come through. I don't believe people can consistently and effectively assist others without truly being in touch with their own issues and history.

Gus: Man, can you sling it.

Charlie: Hey, up until this chapter you did all the talking.

Gus: So you're saying staff just can't come in, do the job, and leave—they have to be touchy-feely soul searchers?

Charlie: If they're not, you guys pay. Yes, I think it's absolutely essential for people who work with troubled kids to know where they're coming from and utilize a strong observing ego. In other words, they must possess the ability to take a step back, psychologically observe what they are doing, and think about the reasons for it. And if their personal history is getting in the way, they should make better choices or get some help. However, it's not the role of the youth care supervisor to do therapy with staff members. Youth care workers should be taught to be aware of the psychological traps inherent in the position and to "check their baggage at the door" before every shift. Workers should also be taught to anticipate the intense feelings they will experience most shifts, such as hate, anger, sexual attraction, inadequacy, and frustration. And they should realize that all feelings are normal, that they must accept and learn from them but never act on them inappropriately. A kid you temporarily "hate" is probably doing a good job of pushing you away and letting you get in touch with the anger she feels toward the world. An attractive sixteen-year-old female who was repeatedly raped could expect a new male counselor to molest her, so she might come on to him, to be in control of when it occurs. And, being a biological creature, he could have a sexual feeling. But of course, he can never, ever act on it. He could be a normal guy who gets sucked into doing something really bad—and illegal—if he hasn't been trained to anticipate and deal with what she's doing. Again, he needs to be told about this stuff before he ever walks onto the floor. Anticipating, identifying, discussing, normalizing, and controlling difficult feelings should be a critical component of the job.

Gus: That's a lot of sentences without a joke. You're putting us to sleep, Jack.

Charlie: Sorry, got carried away.

Gus: So Gus, yours truly, has a lot of you in him?

Charlie: Actually, there's quite a lot of me in you.

Gus: And besides being a teaching fool, I mean tool, I'm also kind of an alter ego on whose shoulders you displace some of your baggage?

Charlie: Correct. And it's okay for me to do so as long as I don't distort what you have to say.

Gus: God, this means we're a lot alike.

Charlie: Shit, I never really thought about that. *Maybe our similarities point out how difficult it is to give up what's comfortable.* I gave you a personality somewhat similar to my own because it was more comfortable for me to devise you in my image.

Gus: Whoa! You swore again, good buddy. I think you're letting a bit too much baggage get in. C'mon, brother, you've got to maintain a positive image.

Charlie: Forget the image. I'm not so sure I want to be identified with a chubby, zit-faced, emotionally disturbed adolescent.

Gus: But I have an IQ of one hundred and sixty-three.

Charlie: Still, this might not look so good.

Gus: Maybe the major parts of you in me aren't so much the disturbed aspects but the personality traits?

Charlie: Hmm, interesting point. Could, in fact, be a lifesaver.

Gus: Even though I'm a screwed-up kid, we can still share similar personality traits—like being loud, foul-mouthed, funny, bright, and passionate—without me completely impugning your reputation.

Charlie: Hey, why did you use the term "screwed up" instead of "fu-k-d up," like you normally would?

Gus: I don't know. Maybe we're resolving some things. Maybe I'm a little less angry.

Charlie: This is weird.

Gus: Totally.

Charlie: It's pretty hard to change one's personality. You are who you are. Adolescents with personality disorders, such as borderline or narcissistic, might not change radically. But with the right kind of help they can modify problem personality traits enough to live happier, more productive lives. There are some great therapies out there for such people. A lot of staff members burn out working with teens who have character disorders because they have unrealistic expectations. They also get easily frustrated with kids who don't respond to rewards and consequences—

really inflexible and explosive kids who often blow over minor issues. The staff members don't realize that many of these kids are hardwired to act the way they do and that you can only modify a personality. I'd like folks to think about this stuff. It's important.

Gus: Yeah, they'll think about it if they're not sleeping by now. I thought this was my book. You're grabbing way too much airtime.

Charlie: You're right. I'm laying it on thick here. But one last thing . . .

Gus: What? Go for it and then zip it. Okay, blubber mouth?

Charlie: People tend to do what they are comfortable doing even though might be less effective. Sometimes what is comfortable is based on history, sometimes it's personality. Often, it's both:

- A behavioristic, somewhat rigid youth care worker might resist a program, abolishing its level system. Too scary.

- A foster mother raised in a puritanical home might be uncomfortable dealing with the sexual issues of her kids.

- A veteran residential director might be uncomfortable about parents spending significant blocks of time on the units. Too radical.

- A shy, laid-back youth care worker might

have trouble working with loud, high-motor dudes.

- Kids who repeatedly tantrum over seemingly minor issues might be telling the world that they aren't wired to handle frustrations and need the environment to change for them to succeed.

Gus: You're taking this deep, man.

Charlie: People aren't bad for being who they are. But they've got to know where they're coming from and how they're constructed (i.e., wired), and be willing to make difficult choices.

Gus: That ain't always easy.

Charlie: Change is a bitch. But to be effective . . .

Gus: We've got to embrace it. Stretch our comfort zones.

Charlie: In the long run, we'll be better off, and so will those we touch.

Gus: As for our personalities?

Charlie: They can change only so much. It's important to understand that.

Gus: I don't buy it.

Charlie: Buy what?

Gus: That you can't radically change your personality, even if it's dysfunctional.

Charlie: Gus, it's a given, a done deal. Some of the new therapeutic approaches hint at being able to "cure" folks with personality disorders, and if they do it would be great.

Gus: Okay, Charles, I won't argue with you.

Charlie: Charles?

Gus: Yes, Charles, pardon me for using nicknames and profanities. I'm terribly mortified by my previous actions.

Charlie: Mortified?

Gus: Yes, I've decided to turn a new leaf. I'm giving up red meat, planting trees in the inner cities, and staying comfortable in my own space. Can you dig this, man?

Charlie: Yeah, I see where you're going. I'm with ya, Gus. We won't be loud anymore.

Gus: Correct.

Charlie: We won't use sarcasm.

Gus: Never.

Charlie: And no more swearing.

Gus: Perish the thought.

Charlie: It's mellow time.

Gus: Right. We're now just two laid-back, easy-going brothers.

Charlie: Yes, this feels good. C'mon, let's chant or something.

Gus: And they said you can't change personality.

Charlie: You think they're buying this?

Gus: Fat chance.

Charlie: That's what I thought.

Gus: Good. Then let's get loud and eat something that's bad for us.

Charlie: Sounds great!

Gus and Charlie bought some greasy hamburgers and . . .

Gus: Wait a second! I've been down this road before. No more fu—. I mean no more friggin' liver. That was low!

Gus and Charlie bought some greasy hamburgers and proceeded to eat the meal of their lives.

Gus: Thanks.

Charlie: No, thank you. You taught me something today.

Gus: Well, then, if you want to show your gratitude let me have some fun in the next chapter.

Charlie: Sorry, Gus. I can't let you influence me in that way. Besides, I haven't even figured out what the next chapter will be about.

Gus: You can't blame a guy for trying.

Charlie: Take it easy, Gus.

Gus: *Asta la vista,* baby.

Charlie ended the fourth chapter. It was tough to write. After revising it approximately one hundred times, he finally felt good about it. He was also feeling pretty good about Gus. Maybe in the next chapter he'd have Gus grow a few inches and lose the zits. Maybe he'd have Gus really meet the perfect foster family. Maybe he'd even get him laid. Yup, that's exactly what will happen. He'll do all of those things!

> Charlie: Hey, who the hell wrote that? Oh, Gus!
>
> Gus: Yes, boss.
>
> Charlie: You wrote that paragraph, didn't you?
>
> Gus: Sorry, *amigo.* It didn't take a genius to break into your computer—but if it did . . .

Gus woke up and looked down. It was gone!

> Gus: Okay, no more writing without your permission.

Gus woke up and looked down. It was gone! The large zit on his chin had somehow disappeared. A change for the better, he thought.

FIVE

BEDTIME, AND A WEE BIT MORE

I am a passenger in the front seat of a fast-moving car. It's hot outside, and I'm sweltering. My exposed skin sticks to the black vinyl. The car reeks of alcohol and something else—rancid meat. Pieces of it are strewn along the back seat like mindless passengers awaiting a second slaughter. I try to roll down the window, but it won't budge. I try again; the handle snaps off violently.

The unseen driver laughs and begins singing, "*Frère Jacques, Frère Jacques, dormez-vous?*" He then stops and cries aloud, "Are you sleeping, Jack? Are you ready for the train?"

I scream but no one hears. The car pulls off the road.

"The train is comin', Gussy."

I jolt upright. My T-shirt is soaked. I feel my heart pounding. The digital clock reads 3:08 a.m. Four hours and fifty-two friggin' minutes until we can get up!

Bedtime sucks when you have a history of being sexually abused. Stimulation, activity, interaction—the diversions of the day—all cease when you get into bed and the lights are extinguished. When you're alone and scared, with nothing to occupy your mind, the bad memories drift back.

For many kids like me, bedtime initiates an inexorable journey down the pathway to hell. The demons wait. They coil behind bedposts, lurk in doorways, and masquerade as harmless shadows. At times, fatigue or sheer determination will fight them off. You either drift off or raise a defiant shield. "I won't think about the bad stuff tonight," you proclaim. Sometimes this works. But sooner or later the demons will clutch your soul and drag you back. Suddenly, you're there, where the abuse all began.

For me, I'm back in my own bed at home. I can hear my mother's boyfriend, Ronald, swaying up the stairs. Mom's not home—she works the night shift at the post office.

Maybe tonight the drunken bastard will fall and break his damn neck, I think. But the bedroom door begins to creak open, and the profile of a grizzled, pathetic creature of a man looms ominously on the wall. The door stops moving, and he begins his approach.

"Gussy-boy, you awake?"

I pretend to be sleeping.

"The train's headin' for the tunnel. Gussy-boy . . . choo choo . . . choo choo . . . got to let the train into the tunnel. If you don't, a boy could get killed."

I figured he meant it. I once saw him shoot a dog. . .

It hurt, but I never let on how much. "Choo choo, train's in real good!" he'd yell.

Ronald went at me for three years before I told. Most of

us kids have Ronalds in our closets. They never go away, and they especially like to come back at night.

Occasionally I'll think I see him during the daytime. At the mall, in school, or at the gym—it can be anywhere. I can be in a great mood but then something about a stranger will remind me of him, and I'll remember the pain. When this happens, I could go in any direction. Sometimes after a painful "association" (as my therapist calls them), I want to kill, to strike out. At other times, I just get down. I'm coming to terms with this, but it's been a struggle.

Kids who have been sexually abused almost always have bad associations. Now and then a new staff member will remind a kid of the jerk who abused him. The kid will usually make life hell for that person. If the kid and that new staff member can work through the shit, if the kid can learn to trust and accept the person who reminds him of the abuser, it usually is a big step forward. I know. I've been that route.

One more thought before bedtime . . . It seems foster parents and staff members in residential centers, even the good ones, tend to get desensitized to abuse. Kid after kid enters an out-of-home placement with a history of being physically, emotionally, or sexually abused. We get lumped together. And because the staff members can see only our difficult, message-sending behaviors and not the abuse we experienced, we become known more for how we act than for how badly we were abused and its effect on us.

Our abuse is notoriously invisible. By contrast, many

years ago a young girl fell down a large drainpipe and the entire country was riveted to news about her condition. Men would come home from work and say, "Hey, honey, did they get the kid out?" When the girl was finally rescued, the whole country rejoiced. People sent cards, money, goods—they couldn't do enough for this little girl. I think they even had a parade in her honor. Well, excuse me! All she did was fall down a damn hole, and everybody loved her. She had three days of pain. I had three years!

If the entire country, including the staff where I'm living now, could have seen firsthand what happened to me, the sympathy and support would have been unreal. Money and compassion would have flowed. Men would say, "Hey, honey, let's send a new bike to that abused kid. Heck, let's give him the car. I can't believe he survived."

When police brutality is caught on tape and goes viral on YouTube, the world screams. Well, who the hell is screaming for us? Do we need to record maggots like Ronald in the act, to get some attention?

Because of our abuse, we do a lot of provocative acting out. It's easy for staff members to get mad at us. It's even easy for us to get mad at us. We forget that the behavior comes from somewhere. A staff member once told me that misbehavior is nothing more than a neon light flashing over a kid's head, announcing, "I need help! I need help!" Not enough people see the lights.

Howie, one of my favorite child care workers, once told me that when he's totally had it with one of us, he goes down to the record room and reads the kid's history. Afterward he feels more compassion and less anger toward the youth. He told me he's had to read mine a number of times. Sometimes Howie can be a wuss.

Jesus, this chapter is all over the place. I guess that's what bedtime is all about. Anyway, prior to getting into bed, or minutes afterward, it's not uncommon for a scared kid to act up or use a delaying tactic to avoid the quiet of the night and the demons that come with it. When I lived in a younger boys unit, bedtime was almost always an event. Ten of us had 9:00 p.m. bedtimes. Prior to bed, we were kept quiet in front of the TV. Around 8:40 p.m., one by one we were sent to the bathroom. Some of us never made it. Getting up from the couch, or from a prone position on the rug, a quick but subtle kick to one of our comrades would get the ball rolling.

"Gus, please take a time out. I saw you kick Chris."

"I did not!"

"Gus, please go to the time-out seat."

"But I didn't do anything! You guys always pick on me!"

Of course I kicked the dude. I had to do something to avoid going to bed. Ronald was waiting.

If I really pushed it, it might be 11:00 p.m. before I finally entered my room. And by then I'd be a lot more tired, possibly from being restrained. Maybe, if I was lucky, I'd fall asleep quickly.

Other kids used different tactics to avoid their Ronalds. Jimmy used the night-light ploy:

"*Staff, my night-light won't work. I can't sleep without a night-light.*"

"*Staff, Peter broke my night-light. I want a night-light!*"

"*Staff, I can't find my night-light. Please, I need a night-light!*"

Peter was equally successful at using the ever popular anti–night-light technique:

"*Staff, I can't sleep with that light on—it's too bright.*"

"*Staff, tell Jimmy to stop playing with the light!*"

"*Staff! I just burned my finger on the light!*"

Mac had an uncanny ability to biologically decompensate exactly at 9:00 p.m. He was a master.

"*Staff, I have an upset stomach, I just puked in the toilet.*"

"*Staff, I'm itchy all over. Do something.*"

"*Staff, I can't move my bowels!*"

Gary, a guy we call the "Big Revealer," used a more psychological approach. When the staff member on duty came into his room to say good night, Gary would spring into action.

> *Staff: Good night, Gary.*
>
> *Gary: Don't leave. I have something important to talk about.*
>
> *Staff: Can't it wait until tomorrow?*
>
> *Gary: No, I can't tell anyone but you. You're the only one I trust.*
>
> *Staff: Okay, what is it?*
>
> *Gary: I want to talk about my abuse.*

Then Gary would make up things or repeat old information over and over. He had a great style and a knack for tugging at heartstrings.

Other kids simply acted out after getting into bed. John would throw things out of his room. Dave was the spitball king. Bruce knocked on walls.

The staff hated bedtime almost as much as the kids did. Intellectually, most of them knew we acted out because of our fears. But when you're on your twelfth hour and you're tired, knocking on walls and throwing spitballs pisses you off.

Bedtime was also tough on staff for another reason. When you're putting ten troubled kids to bed, you have to be damn careful how much time you spend with each one of them. If a staff member spent ten extra minutes talking to Gary, we all wanted ten extra minutes. There was no way for staff members to give us the time and nurturance we all needed. Ideally, each one of us should have had our own staff member sitting with us, assuring us, telling us a bedtime story, whatever it took. But with ten kids and only two staff that wasn't possible. The only way to guarantee extra attention was to act up or develop a good ploy.

The unfortunate reality is that abused kids need a lot more TLC at bedtime than residential treatment centers are set up to provide. Many staff members go home when the kids go to bed. Maybe agencies can't afford to keep too many people on duty at this time. If they could, there would be more compassion. As it is, I think staff members with good hearts are more frustrated at bedtime than any other time of the day, because their hands are tied.

I'd guess that all troubled kids in group homes and residential treatment centers want attention. Now and then we hear the famous put-down "You're just looking for attention," and we're made to feel bad for doing so. But when you live with a dozen other needy kids, you're not always going to get the attention you deserve. Remember, most of us end up in residential treatment because of abuse and neglect. We never got the attention we deserved in the past. So we ask for even more in the present.

It's funny. If you asked someone with normal intelligence where would be the best place to treat a troubled kid with behavior problems, the answer would not be, "With ten or twelve other kids who have similar problems."

Technically, if you put troubled kids with "normal" kids, they'd get better a lot quicker. Otherwise, all hell can break loose. We feed off each other. We learn new ways to act out from our associates. We learn about self-abuse, physical restraint, and the other 101 ways to act out we never knew existed. The only reason I can figure that group homes and residential treatment centers exist as they do is money. It wouldn't be cost effective to have group homes with only two or three kids (this I know because of some calculations I do for the Highland Hills business manager, Ruth). The rate the state pays the group home for each kid wouldn't support such a small establishment. According to Ruth, there need to be eight to fifteen kids in a unit to make it financially feasible. That's eight to fifteen kids with only two to four staff members on duty—it's not enough. Sure, good treatment does occur in residential centers and group homes for troubled kids even with the lousy ratios. I've seen a lot of kids do pretty well here at Highland Hills. But I bet they'd do even better if the staff-child ratios were better.

People who work in residential settings for troubled kids need to be aware of certain realities. Here's a biggie (I figured it out with my therapist, Ellen): the treatment a program offers (i.e., how they talk to kids, the rules they develop, who they take in, and their philosophy) is very much based on its resources, not on what is therapeutically ideal. And nowhere is this more evident than at bedtime (I figured this out on my own), a scary, anxious period of the day. Common sense would dictate that every program put high numbers of staff on duty to ease this period for the kids. But financial realities don't allow for it.

So what happens? Well, at Highland Hills bedtime shenanigans are squashed big time because the program can't afford to have kids fooling around at night since there wouldn't be enough staff members to handle the situation, which would threaten the overall safety of the children. Safety, the "Big S," always comes first. So if a kid is caught fooling around after bedtime he often gets a major consequence. He could be grounded for the day, lose certain privileges, and might have to go to bed earlier for a while.

Now, is this therapeutic? I don't think so. What *would* be is five awake staff members on duty all night. A kid experiencing nighttime difficulties could then be attended to quickly, and appropriately separated, if indicated, without major consequences. This would be the therapeutic ideal.

If staff members better understand how their program's resources influence their treatment techniques, the kids will benefit. If, for instance, a program needs to administer heavy consequences for bedtime problems because of the staffing ratio, an informed worker who is aware of the resource issue might strongly advocate for better staffing patterns. I think new staff members (and probably old ones) don't realize how much their program's lack of resources influences treatment. They are led to believe that what they do is what is right. But I don't think so!

Two other things happen at bedtime: sexual stuff and bed-wetting (which are generally exclusive events). At times, kids get sexual at night, particularly the adolescents. Programs like the one at Highland Hills try everything they can to stop this kind of activity, but most, I assume, realize there's only so much they can do.

Think about it. Eight to twelve boys (or girls) are placed in a residential setting for emotionally disturbed kiddos. They are given limited freedom because the program and society (in this case represented by the state Social Services Department) don't trust them (nor should they). After all, each one of us has demonstrated significant behavior problems, often of a sexual nature. (Prior to coming to Highland Hills, I had a habit of exposing myself on billboards.)

We are put away in this "home" for troubled boys where

some of us will live through most of our adolescence. We are told to abide by a certain set of rules. We are advised that sex play is forbidden. We are given limited latitude with the babes, due to liability concerns and distrust. So, what happens when the hormones start to gyrate and the outlets are out of reach? Well, masturbation helps. But after a while your hand gets tired and you yearn for more.

Adding fuel to the fire is, of course, our shared history. When you've been sexually abused, your hormone switch gets turned on early. Sex is on your mind—a lot. Someone (the abuser) started something with you, and now you feel driven at times to finish it off right, to "master" the experience. Yet unfortunately the mastering, which can start shortly after the abuse, may continue for a lifetime if the right help doesn't come along.

In general, we're confused as hell about this sex thing. I think a lot of prostitutes, male and female, were abused as kids, and are now trying to master their hurt and shame by controlling sex, which was forced upon them. I ran away last year and stayed with three prostitutes in the city. Our histories were dishearteningly similar. Given all this, it's somewhat understandable and predictable that abused kids living in group care situations are going to get involved sexually with one another. If the home is all boys, then it will be the boys getting it on. Are we homosexual? With most of us it's probably too early to tell. I do think that given the lack of love and intimacy we have all generally experienced, the sexual interactions we have are motivated more by the pain of emptiness and the ramifications of abuse than any true proclivity toward partners of the same sex. In simple terms, we take it where we can get it.

I'm not saying it's right that some of us get involved in clandestine sexual liaisons either with the same or opposite sex. Getting involved, particularly in our early teens, if not younger, often serves to confuse or shame us even more. But sometimes the urge is just too great to fight off.

Obviously, bedtime is when most sexual activity is going to happen. Some kids try to force themselves on others. Some kids are easy targets. This reality adds to the bedtime tension most of us experience. It also adds to staff uneasiness. Some of the staff members, particularly the men, have a real hard time when they catch two boys in the act. They freak.

I would guess seeing two boys fooling around is grossly out of the norm for these staff members. They see it as quite perverted. What some don't understand is that this kind of behavior might be closer to the "norm" for the boys in question.

Because of AIDS, the sex thing has grown even more intense. We all get condoms and lots of education, but the sixty-four-thousand-dollar question is: Will we heed the advice? Some of us are so angry we don't give a darn if we get it. Some of us, I think, would see getting AIDS as the truest confirmation of our "no good" status. *"It figures I got it."* And a lot of us just block out the whole thing. After all, many of us have been repeatedly abused in the biblical sense. We might be HIV positive and already doomed. Me, I've avoided getting tested like the plague. Denial, one of my favorite defense mechanisms, sometimes works. Then again, defense mechanisms, from what I've read, are supposed to be unconscious, so maybe I'm getting closer to this issue. Great, another gray cloud over my already dark horizon.

Actually, what really worries me about this AIDS thing is not so much the kids but the staff. It's already hard to work with abused, angry kids. If there isn't enough AIDS training and support for staff members, we could start being treated like lepers. I had a nightmare the other night. I was in the movie *Ben Hur* and was living in the leper colony with Ben's mother and sister. At the end of the movie, when the rain changed them back, I got worse!

All the staff use gloves now when dealing medically with us. I guess this makes sense. But it seems some staff members won't even wipe their own asses without wearing the damn things. If it appears this issue has got me on edge, then the perception is accurate. I'm scared stiff. With my luck, I probably got it.

And yes, bed-wetting is pretty common among us kids, especially at night. It's nice if the staff members are compassionate about this since most of us are embarrassed when it occurs. One of my foster mothers made me wear diapers at night. God, did that suck. Before I left her home, I pissed out the window and it hit the mailman. I was in another foster placement within twenty-four hours. I was a "Special Delivery."

Four years ago Lee, a crazy, scared little kid, was admitted due to some heavy abuse he was takin'. He was given the bedroom next to mine and would wet the bed four or five times a night. He kept the staff up all hours changing his sheets. They were getting worn out (both the staff and the sheets).

After about a week, it was time for the unit director, Ellie, to sleep over. The kids loved her, and she was sharp, so they never got anything past her. Well, after Lee got up for the second time to have his sheets changed Ellie got smart. She followed Lee back into his room and observed the fully soaked sheets. She then bent down and rubbed her index finger along the wet fabric, raised her finger to her mouth, and tasted. "Doesn't taste like urine to me," she bellowed. Little Lee turned white. The poor kid had been sneaking water into his room and feigning the bed-wetting. He just couldn't go very long without having a staff member in his face. I applauded his ingenuity and began to look out for the little guy.

One last thing about bedtime concerns psychotropic medication, little pills administered at night to help us sleep. I've overheard staff members talking about pills the shrinks put us on. Some staff don't like the idea that we take anything. I think it's an ego thing—they want us to improve the old-fashioned way, through hard work and perseverance. Actually, it seems like a lot of us are helped by these medications. They don't cure us, but they seem to help us do the work we need to do, or at least get to sleep with less difficulty.

Some kids are resistant to going on meds. They've heard a lot of weird things about them.

Some kids also have parents with misconceptions or a downright mistrust of meds. They discourage taking them, or simply don't allow their kids to take the pills. I think this is a damn shame. The pain at bedtime can be unreal. If there's a safe way of easing the agony, I say, "Go for it." It worked for me. I used to take an antidepressant, desipramine. It helped, and there were no side effects.

Well, I think I've said as much as I can about bedtime, and I guess a wee bit more. It has the potential to be a real nightmare. Some kids can handle it; some can't. Staff members need a lot of support to support us at night. I hope they get it.

The car is traveling down the same familiar road. Everything outside appears gray and motionless. Inside, the air is stifling. The driver's eyes are fixated on the road ahead. His breath smells of bourbon; his haggard face wears a baleful signature. His foot presses gingerly on the accelerator, thrusting the six-cylinder vehicle ominously forward. My heart pounds in an excruciating rhythm. I gasp for air as I begin to panic. Suddenly, the driver jerks the wheel to the right, and the white walls connect with a dirt road hidden beneath the branches of a large pine. "We're almost there, Gussy-boy . . . trains revving up. Oh, Momma, I feel the heat of the engine." Abruptly, the car skids to a stop. The driver turns to me and reveals a grotesque, almost toothless grin. "Get the tunnel ready, Gussy-boy," he now taunts as his hands begin to undo his tattered trousers. "Not this time, scumbag!" I cry out with vengeful ecstasy. With all the force my abused frame can muster, I drive my fist into the monster's piteous face, feeling the shattered particles of his nose scatter beneath my penetrating flesh. A scream pierces the air as he grabs for his wounded feature. I lurch again and deliver one more mammoth blow to his face. It knocks his fuckin' head right off his body. "Holy shit," I proclaim.

Suddenly a large hand grasps my shoulder. I jolt upright and look into the eyes of the on-duty staff member.

"Are you okay, Gus? You were doing a lot of tossing and turning in your bed . . . another nightmare?"

"I'm all right. Thanks."

I lower my head to the pillow as a small smile crosses my lips. I beat him—tonight.

SIX
FRIENDSHIP

Everyone needs friends. Friends get you through hard times. Friends make you laugh. Friends give you wedgies. Friends loan you money. Friends care about you.

When I first got to Highland Hills, four years ago, I had never had a best friend. There are lots of us who come here never having connected with another kid. We wear this failure like a neon light on a black wall.

Two years ago, Bobby and I snuck down to the kitchen after tuck-in and pigged out on some cold chili. Man, we farted all night. God, did we laugh. I'll never forget that night. Bobby was my first buddy.

Abused and neglected kids need to take care of themselves first—before they can worry about someone else's needs. It's a full-time job. When I lived at home, I spent most of my time trying to survive and I never had time to think about anything else. I worried about getting fed, having enough clothes, not getting beaten, my mother's drinking, sexual abuse, and whether the heat would come on. Sometimes I worried about disappearing. Life was awful.

The professionals used such terms to describe me as "egocentric" and "narcissistic," often in front of me, as if I weren't there. At first, I didn't know what the two terms meant. *"Maybe they mean I'm unique and special,"* I thought, but I was in for a rude awakening.

Unfortunately, I was far from unique. When I got to Highland Hills, I noticed that most of the kids were just like me, into themselves and socially underdeveloped. I noticed one other thing: we all suffered terribly because of this. Most of us feel imprisoned in loneliness.

One day I was getting picked on by Carl Spooner. Carl was big and crazy. I was scared of that boy, and he knew it. Carl was making fun of my weight. I was on the verge of tears. Well, Bobby happened to stroll in from a home visit just as Carl was really letting me have it. Before you could say, "Holy shit!" Bobby ran at Carl, grabbed a chunk of his hair, and proceeded to bite his nose. I never heard a kid yell so loud. Two staff members had to pull Bobby off of him. Carl seemed in shock. He had been out-crazed. The bastard never bothered me again. No kid had ever stuck up for me like Bobby did that day. I'll never forget it.

Kids come to group care hungry to relate. But we have lousy table manners, if you catch my drift. One day we're buddy-buddy with a kid; the next day we're fighting. Relationships are never sustained.

Once when I was hanging out in the library—I had a

crush on Latisha Watkins, the twenty-nine-year-old librarian—I scanned a few books on developmental psychology and peer relations. One, written by a dude named Sullivan, talked about how important it was for a young child, between five and twelve years old, to develop a first best friend, or "chum." According to Sully, when a kid makes his first best friend he has to give up some of his selfishness and egocentrism to enjoy and maintain the friendship. He learns about the normal give-and-take of a sustained relationship. Around age five, peer relations become very important. Instead of having all needs met by Mommy or Daddy, the fivish dude looks to friends to meet key needs. According to the theory, it feels so good to have a best friend that a kid will readily relinquish even intense egocentrism.

Bobby and I used to count our pubic hairs. At first we used a magnifying glass. I remember one time using the glass outside. God, I almost burnt it off!

The typical five-year-old—if I understand the literature correctly—must emotionally separate from his folks and learn to fend for himself, with the support of his pals. The kid becomes a real little person. If he's too into himself ("me, me, me"), due to wiring or certain primitive needs never being met, and can't get along with the other kids or teachers, he's gonna be in heavy you know what, according to the theorists.

Well, Sully and the others were on to something. When I hit first grade, I was light years behind the others developmentally. I simply wasn't ready for the normal give-and-take. When it came to getting along, I couldn't put anyone else's needs ahead of my own. Looking out for number one was all I knew, so it was my job—and I did it with gusto. The pain of not fitting in and being teased was unreal. I hated going to school. I felt like a misfit. I often tantrummed at breakfast, hoping to be kept home. I knew most of the kids didn't like me and talked behind my back. I even became a little paranoid. As a result, I was scapegoated, got in tons of fights, and was bounced from two public schools. (I couldn't believe it when the Angier school expelled me for throwing a kid's coat on the ground and stepping on it. How the hell did I know the kid was still in it?)

Bobby had burn marks on his arm. He never talked about them. I don't think they got there by accident. The better I got to know Bobby, the more those marks bothered me.

You see, abused and neglected kids don't necessarily act out because of what happened to us. We often act out because the abuse and neglect caused serious ramifications—like not being able to make and sustain a goddamn friendship because we're so "me, me, me"—too busy taking care of number one because no one else has.

Bobby was discharged from the program eight months ago. I really miss him. When I was with him, I felt cool. I felt connected. Life was easier and more fun after hooking up with Bobby. I don't hear from him much anymore. He's getting on with his life. Carl's still here, and he's got this little scar on his nose. I won't forget Bobby.

Making friends is crucial to our development, yet kids like me are frequently unprepared to do so. Socially, we're often like bulls in a china shop (though I'm not sure, since I've never seen a china shop).

A new kid, Marcus, came to Highland Hills a few months ago. He has to be in control of everything, and he's a real know-it-all. None of the kids like him. He won't say it, but he's hurtin' inside. He's lonely. I know, I was there.

So, how does residential treatment help us improve our social skills? Get some buddies? I think it depends on how much they understand the importance of friendship building. Sometimes friendship building is sacrificed, or simply not prioritized, because an agency lacks the resources to facilitate "enhanced peer interactions," or because it does not place enough value on this aspect of "milieu therapy." Some agencies do not emphasize friendship building in or outside of their program because the process can at times be disruptive. For instance, say two kids are arguing over something. To "quiet" the situation, a staff member might intervene and quickly settle the matter. Such an intervention would keep the lid on, to use a popular term in the residential world, but would not help the two children learn to resolve their differences.

One day, Marcus is going to find a best friend. It will be an intoxicating experience that will make him feel great. There's nothing like a best friend—especially your first one. I think everyone remembers their first best friend.

Staff members in places like Highland Hills generally don't want a whole lot of acting out from the kiddos. And who can blame them? It's hard just getting through a "routine" day. So sometimes staff members act in ways that serve their needs more than the needs of the kids. It's often a necessary evil. Sometimes they just don't have the training, time, or energy to promote and facilitate healthier peer relations.

Last year I ran away with three kids because they were the three coolest kids at Highland Hills. I didn't want to run away. But at the time I wasn't feeling very good about myself and it felt great to be accepted by them.

Here at Highland Hills, they're trying something new to help kids improve socialization skills. They call it "Duo Therapy." One therapist or senior youth care worker sees two kids at the same time once or twice a week, both of whom have had trouble making and keeping friends. It seems like it's working. Carl, the bully, was matched with Andrew. They couldn't be more different. Carl's loud and bossy; Andrew's quiet and meek. Yet they seem to be hitting it off. I heard Andrew tell Carl to "shut up and listen" the other day. I was shocked. At first, it looked from his eyes like Carl would deck him. But he paused, and then, to my amazement, he shut up and listened, not wanting to blow it. The two are becoming friends.

Friendship is powerful.

My roommate Hector is currently my best friend. We talk a lot about girls and doing it. We also sneak in cigarettes from time to time. I sometimes hear Hector crying at night. He really misses his family but remembers the pain. Sometimes, to help him, I'll sit next to his bed and read a book out loud. Also, he helps me when I'm down. We need each other. We're important to each other. Although we're both hurtin', there's a joy in what we have together.

SEVEN
MOM'S PERSPECTIVE

The letter was on my bed when I got home. It was thick. At first, I didn't know who it was from. But as I got closer to the bed, the scribbled penmanship startled my scrabbled brain. Mother. She was making contact. Again.

Nervously, I opened the envelope. A bead of sweat formed and departed from my brow. My heart raced. And that old knot returned to my stomach. *Mother*—a word I associated with a range of adjectives, including all expletives, was now resonating in my brain.

"What does she want? What's it gonna be this time?" Hope? Despair? Anger? Loneliness? My hands shook as my contorting brain tried to focus on her words. Slowly, I lowered my butt to the mattress, kicked off my shoes, summoned my courage, and began to read:

Dear Gus,

It's been almost six months since I last saw you. I'm living in a small town in Vermont named Castle Stone. I'm staying with a friend, Bonnie. She and I used to waitress together at the White Horse. She's got a small house on a pretty little lake. I'm working the night shift at the local post office. I haven't had a drink in four months. I go to AA meetings twice a week. For the first time in a long time, I'm feeling good.

I know. You've heard it all before. And maybe this time won't be any different, but maybe it will. Look, kid, I don't expect you to have much faith left in your old mom, especially after the last go-round. But there are things I want you to know, feelings I want to share. Please, Gus, read this entire letter, and then think what you want. It's important. I'm going to tell you things I've never had the courage to share. And please don't send this letter back with the grammar corrected. I hate when you do that. You know, it can be somewhat intimidating having such a brainiac for a son.

Okay, let's start with a recap. You don't see me for five years, and then one day I'm at Highland Hills and want to get you back. We start visiting and going to therapy together, and then before long they talk about you coming home—for good. Well, you know the rest. I begin drinking again. I screw up at work. I don't show up for a number of home visits, and then, I'm history—again. The Big Disappointer, that's me.

Gus, you have every reason to hate me. I've set you up more times than I want to remember. But for what it's worth, I want to do some explaining. If it doesn't help you, at least it will help me.

I really wanted us to be a family again, but I freaked. Thinking about being a parent to an adolescent, about making decisions, about doing it right, I became over-whelmed. I thought I was ready, but I wasn't. Living in that new town and not knowing anyone didn't help. I guess I could have used more support. But I didn't know how to get it. So I turned to the bottle, the wrong kind of support.

Gus, I've told you about my childhood, but I never told you everything. Thinking back, I don't have many pleasant memories. Hell, for most of my adult life I've tried to keep my past blocked away. But lately, with the help of my new therapist, Marge, I've been doing a lot of digging. She thinks it might be helpful for you to hear where I've been.

I told you that I was sexually abused by my mother's brother for almost seven years. I mentioned how he threatened to kill me if I told. But I never talked to you much about my mother. I loved her. And I hated her. She should have protected me. When she finally found out about the abuse, she denied that it happened. She said she would have known. But she did know.

My mother never wanted me. And I don't think she ever let me forget it. According to her, there were four guys who could have been my father. Two of them were strangers—one-night standeroos. She was supposed to get an abortion but got smashed the day before the procedure and was too hung over to get it done. After that, she fell in love with a new guy who wasn't too thrilled about her being pregnant. As soon as I was born, he took off. My mother was still a teenager then, more into partying than mothering. During my first four years, I was bounced from relative to relative. I didn't stay in one place for very long.

In case you're wondering, I found out a lot of this

information from Aunt Helen. She's still living in Waltham, Massachusetts. As you know, Helen has always been my "old reliable," the only person I could ever truly count on. Lately, we've been writing and talking on the phone and she's been helping me put the pieces together.

Anyways, when I was four my mother took me back (the welfare payments enticed her). From what I can remember, we actually had some okay years. I mean, no one got hurt, and we stayed in the same place for a while. But my mother never really treated me as a daughter—more like a peer, a roommate. I thought that was how all mothers treated their daughters. I didn't realize how disastrous this was until very recently, when I began working with Marge.

I guess I lost—or never had—the opportunity to be a little kid. I was too worried and had too many big responsibilities looking after my mother. While all the other kids were playing house, I was keeping house. As a result, I never had what the other kids got: the privilege to experience the world through the eyes of a little girl, to receive the emotions that flow to all such aspiring young Barbies. So I've had to grieve my lost childhood. To be a healthy adult, it sure helps to have had a healthy childhood. Well, pal, I didn't. And, I guess, neither did you.

I can see now that how I treated you was very similar to how I got treated. I'm sorry about that. I never realized what was going on. I was simply doing the best I could with what I had, which wasn't much.

Actually, the whole thing is kind of ironic. Because I had to be more grown up as a little girl, I ended up becoming more immature as I got older. In fact, as a teenager (and, at times, as an adult) I often acted like a bratty little twit—obnoxious, impulsive, loud, and unruly. All the behaviors I never got to unleash when I lived with my mother and they would have appeared somewhat "normal." Of course, the sexual abuse didn't help either.

Uncle Billy came to live with us when I was seven. He had a good job with the gas company and helped my mother with the bills. He also helped himself to me. He was an alcoholic. And he was scary. You never could predict what he'd say or do. Once, after getting into an argument with his boss, he came home and beat the hell out of my mother and me. She pleaded with me not to tell anyone what had happened. She had become dependent on Uncle Billy. The needlemarks on her arms, which she called "hives," kept them connected. Years later she spoke to me about her heroin period, after I got busted shooting the same crap.

Not long after Uncle Billy moved in, he started coming on to me. At first, it was through compliments: "My, my, doesn't our little girl look pretty today" and "Jesus, just look at our little Mary. The boys will be fighting all day over you." Initially, I kind of liked the attention since I wasn't used to receiving praise. I never thought I was pretty. No one ever told me I was. Aunt Helen always made me feel special, but I didn't see her too much. So, it was nice to hear Uncle Billy say such things.

But soon his words no longer felt good. It was his eyes that changed them. He'd say the same things but would stare right through me. I began to avoid him. Then one night when my mother was out, working as a waitress at the local dive, he came into my room and raped me. I was seven. The pain was unbearable. And he smelled something awful. Afterward, he returned with a large, shiny hunting knife and explained specifically where he would cut if I ever told.

Uncle Billy lived with us, on and off, for seven years. And he was on and off me for all that time. I never told anybody, not even the few friends I had. So many times I wanted to tell my mother. But she was so weak and he was so threatening. I hated her for bringing this man into our home. Even though it hadn't been perfect, the three years I had lived alone with her, from ages four to seven, were probably the best of my childhood.

Gus, I wanted so desperately for my mother to love me, to save me, but it never came out right. She was a very nervous woman with a terrible self-image. Whenever the pressure got too much, she turned to the bottle or to drugs. Only now do I realize how hurtin' she really was. I spent a lot of my youth getting her to bed and dressing her for work. Her quiet appreciation of my usefulness seemed to sustain me. But that's a pretty shitty way to get raised.

At fourteen, I ran away from home. I couldn't take it anymore. I stayed with Molly O'Hara, the one true friend I had. Molly eventually told her parents why I had run off, and they called the police. I was put in a temporary foster home while an investigation was conducted. Uncle Billy at first denied everything, and Mom supported him and refused to believe me. But Uncle Billy eventually admitted the abuse and copped a plea. According to Aunt

Helen, Billy kind of cracked up in front of one of the investigators. Apparently, he started screaming, "No, Grandpa! No, Grandpa!"

It turns out both Billy and my mother had been sexually molested by their mother's dad. A nice legacy, eh?

Billy got six months in jail and then a lengthy probation and was ordered to attend therapy sessions, as well as weekly AA meetings. He was also restricted from being near me. I still don't know why the bastard got off so easy.

With Billy out of the house, I was returned home. I was also hooked up with a therapist from the local mental health clinic. The first thing my mother said when I came home was, "You happy 'bout what you've done?" "What I did," I screamed. "That bastard fucked me for seven years, and you did nothing." I stormed out of the house and ran to the clinic. Ann, my therapist, sat with me as I cried for forty-five minutes. She then called my mother, who reluctantly joined us. It was the first time I had ever seen my mother cry for the pain I suffered.

Ann was very patient and warm toward my mother. She let her blow off steam by putting me down before getting my mother to fess up. All of a sudden, my mother was bawlin' her eyes out and asking God to forgive her. Over the next six months, Ann, my mother, and I had some amazing sessions. At one point my mother claimed she was furious with me for letting the abuse go on without me saying anything. When Ann pressed her about this, she was able, with Ann's help, to see that much of her anger was due to *her* inability to say anything when she had been repeatedly molested.

She also revealed how guilty she had felt for remaining quiet about Uncle Billy. She had a "feeling" something was going on.

Six months later, Ann left the clinic. Mom and I were devastated. We loved that lady. The new therapist, Rebecca, was not our cup of tea. After a few months, we both stopped showing up. A few months later, Mom was drinking heavily again and we began having horrible arguments.

I was about fifteen at the time and had started drinking and getting laid by any guy who smiled at me. I felt like such a piece of shit, was so empty, that sex with any guy who wanted me filled a need. I made some awful decisions in those days. My mother, at times, tried to discipline me, something she was not too familiar doing. But my rage and her guilt left Mom weak and ineffective.

At eighteen, I got hooked on heroin and was ordered to a drug clinic. I knew my mother had been into heroin. By doing heroin, I was identifying with Mom. When a kid acts like a parent—even in a bad way—it makes that kid feel closer to the parent, I've learned. And of course acting out helps kids get back at their parents for screwing them over. I think when kids have been injured by their parents they go through life continually looking to heal the wounds. Sometimes the healing can take place even if the parents aren't around anymore. Other times the attempt to heal is misguided, like when it involves copying a destructive behavior.

Up until now, I've told you very little about your father, only that I hardly knew him. I deflected your attempts to press me for more information. I had my reasons. Let me now fill in some of the pieces for you.

While at the drug clinic, I met and fell in love with your father. His name was Fritz Studelmeyer. He had entered the clinic a few weeks before I got there. I became pregnant with you while Fritz and I were at the clinic. He was an amazing guy. He could multiply three-digit numbers by three-digit numbers in his head as quick as a calculator. He could also speak fluent Chinese, which he had learned while bussing at a Chinese restaurant. When no one was looking, Fritz would call the local Chinese laundry and complain, in Chinese, about them using too much starch. He was a funny guy. He was also very depressed. His moods would turn on a dime, but I thought he was the greatest guy I had ever met.

We were discharged at the same time, and two weeks later we got married. I was really happy. For the first time in a long time, I was clean and looking forward to the future. Fritz got a job at Radio Shack, and I began waitressing. We lived with his older brother, Ziggy.

Well, one day I was at work and the phone rang. It was the hospital, saying Fritz was dead of a heroin overdose. I freaked out and spent two weeks in the psycho ward at the local hospital. My mother visited me once. She couldn't handle my depression, probably because she couldn't handle her own. Luckily, Aunt Helen offered to let me stay with her in her tiny place when the two weeks were up.

After a few cramped months with Helen, I returned home to live with my mother. Because my mother never really wanted me, she wasn't too thrilled with you growing in my belly. We fought a lot. But occasionally we shared some nice moments. Mom recounted her battle with drug addiction, and, even though it continued, we drew a little closer to each another.

Then I met Ronald, who wasn't much to look at and was an alcoholic. But I was six months pregnant and couldn't stay with my mother any longer because the tension was becoming unbearable. Ronald was my meal ticket. He had inherited his parents' home and made a decent living doing odd jobs and collecting trash. He didn't seem to mind my being pregnant, so I moved in with him and had you.

Before long, he started to beat me, all the while complaining about dinner being late, me being too fat, or "that fuckin' kid crying again." At first, the beatings weren't so bad; he'd use an open hand. Later, the bastard used his fists. I should have picked you up and left the first time he hurt me, but I didn't. Since Uncle Billy used to beat me, I figured most men were that way and most girls deserved it.

Gus, it's taken me a long time, and a lot of therapy and reading, to see how screwed up I was. No one deserves to be abused. Up until now I've denied abusing you sexually. I've refused to talk about it. I wouldn't let your therapist at Highland Hills get near the subject. I know my denial, as it's been called, has hurt you even more. I'm sorry.

Tragically, you were abused by Ronald and by me. The longer I stayed with Ronald, the more I coped by drinking and doing cocaine. When you were six, I got fired by the post office for coming in loaded. I "celebrated" my firing by getting even more wasted. And it was in that crazy state that I did things to you, sexual things, with Ronald that I will regret forever. I don't remember everything. But I remember enough. Damn it, Gus, I am so sorry for all of this . . . and what that monster did to you. When I woke the next morning, I couldn't look myself in the mirror. I do recall throwing up—and not because of the booze. I confronted Ronald, and that's when I found out he had been sexually abusing you for two goddamn years. What you must have gone through!

For one brief, repugnant moment that will torture me as long as I live, I became my Uncle Billy. I did to you what had been done to me. And in that moment it felt good. That's sick. Marge is helping me understand how it could have happened and how to cope with the shame.

Look, Gus, a bad history doesn't take someone off the hook in terms of being responsible for their actions, so I'm not going to ask for your forgiveness. Just perhaps for a little understanding so we can move on. Marge says we've got to put our memories, our pain, in perspective.

After I found out that Ronald had been sexually abusing you, I pulled you out of that house as quick as I could. I had nowhere to go but back to my mother's. She had just married Barney, who worked part-time at the local hardware store and also collected disability payments from the government. While he was serving in the army, a jeep ran over his foot and crushed his heel, so he still walked with a limp. Barney was an alcoholic but had been sober for four years.

I'm sure you remember Barney. He was actually a good guy and good for my mother. At first, the two of you hit it off pretty good. But when my mother heard what happened to you, she called yours truly every name under the sun, and Barney had to restrain her to keep her from killing me. She then kicked me out of the house, saying I wasn't fit to be a mother. Man, wasn't that the pot calling the kettle black? But how could I argue? Even though I had been drunk out of my gourd, I had sexually abused you. I had also failed to protect you for three goddamn years while Ronald did his thing.

Mom insisted that I give up custody of you. She threatened to have me and Ronald prosecuted if I didn't. I hated her for that. She was sticking up for you but she had never stuck up for me. I was enraged, but my guilt and remorse inhibited me from fighting. I simply signed over custody of you to my mother and let Barney and her raise you.

Gus, I know you've said you don't like to talk much about those years when you bounced from me to my mother then to numerous foster homes, finally landing at Highland Hills. I know they weren't easy for you. They weren't easy years for me, either.

I hated visiting you when you lived with my mother. She never let me forget what Ronald and I had done to you. I felt like a piece of crap every time I walked through the door. But who was she to cast stones? Uncle Billy went at me for seven years, and she did nothing! Barney tried to get her to lighten up, but she never changed. I think she saw raising you as a way to make up for the mistakes she made with me. This time she'd get it right. Wrong.

My mother wasn't emotionally equipped to raise you, even with Barney's help. I know you lasted two years with them, but don't blame yourself for the acting out that caused your removal to foster care. You simply had too much to deal with. God, what an awful time that must have been for you.

When you were eight and ordered into foster care, I moved out of state. I couldn't bear to see you being raised by strangers who would probably be judging me every time I'd come to visit. I knew what they'd probably be thinking.

"So that's Gus's mother, the one who sexually abused him."

"Here comes the ex-addict to visit her son."

"What kind of mother abuses her own kid?"

"What kind of mother lets another person abuse her kid for three years."

"Can we trust this woman not to hurt her kid again?"

"Is she drunk?"

Foster care is supposed to be a temporary thing, but I had heard that some foster parents get downright possessive about "their" kids and turn their noses up at the biological parents. I wasn't ready to deal with that.

I was ashamed of who I had become. But I was also angry about my past. If life had been different for me, I would surely have been different. Anyways, I just ran away from everything—you, my mother, the memories. But as you know, you really can't get away from this stuff. At some point, the music stops and you have to deal with it.

In Maine, where I landed, I made a lot of bad decisions. I couldn't forget you, my mother, the abuse (mine, as well as yours), that scumbag Ronald. My brain seemed haunted by the evil from my past.

For the first few years there, I drifted from job to job and increasingly turned to booze to fight off the demons. Then, when money got scarce I became a two-bit criminal—a little shoplifting here, a little burglary there. I think I wanted to get caught and punished. I hated myself. It was a chore getting up in the morning; sometimes I didn't. Life was gray, the days dragged on, and the hole I was digging grew wider and deeper. Finally, mercifully, I got caught trying to pass some phony checks. I was sent to the Women's State Penitentiary for eighteen months.

It was awful. But, as they say, it turned out to be a "sobering" experience. There I met Claire LaFrancois, a guard stationed in my cell block. She actually cared about the inmates and helped me get my act back together.

She, too, had been sexually abused as a kid. We would talk about the ramifications of this. She related a lot of what she and her therapist had worked on together. Sometimes we'd just look at each other and cry.

For the first time, I started to think it wasn't all my fault. Ann, my former therapist, had tried to work with me on this. But hearing from someone else who had been sexually abused, who had struggled with the same issues, helped a lot. Claire said that the prison was full of women who had been sexually abused and that people have no idea how prevalent sexual abuse is. The other thing she said which made a lot of sense was that in homes where there is sexual abuse there's a higher probability of general dysfunction. In other words, it isn't just the sexual abuse that screws kids up; it's the abuse coupled with inadequate parenting. The prisons, according to Claire, are full of little souls crying out for their mommies to love them better, and acting out because the love never comes, or isn't enough.

I think having a good childhood is like having a nice foundation for a home. Without a strong foundation, you can't build much higher. If you do, it's at risk of crumbling. Gus, I've crumbled more times than I'd like to remember. I do think I can go higher, and I'm working to understand my past without blaming myself or my mother. When you stop the blaming, the picture becomes clearer. I think that through understanding and support people who have suffered terrible trauma, like me (like us), can get our foundations in place and grow stronger.

In prison, I thought a lot about you and decided I would get you back. Claire helped me believe I could. When I got out, I moved closer to you, got a job, began attending AA meetings, and then, after six months, I called Highland Hills and said, "Hello, Highland Hills, this is Gus's mother. I want my kid back!" It took another four months before I was allowed to visit due to red tape. The state had custody of you. A good bit of legal maneuvering had to take place before I got the green light. And then, I was one scared mom.

As you are well aware, things started out pretty good. Even though I had not seen you for five years, you were ready to give me a shot. Sure, it was awkward at first, yet we seemed to work through the "getting to know you again" jitters.

But I hated coming to pick you up. Every time I drove into the driveway, that big sign reading, "Highland Hills Children's Home" spoke to me, saying, "Welcome, you failure!" While everybody inside was so good and pure, I was a dirtbag, a parent who had abused her only son. Even though the staff who worked with you all seemed pretty nice, I wondered what they were thinking. It was made pretty clear to me that if I hadn't shown up you would have been matched with a new foster family. I think they even had one picked out. Even though she tried to hide it, I think your therapist, Ellen, was upset that I had returned. Christ, I proved them right! I let you down again—because it got too damn scary.

Even though I never spent more than fifteen to twenty minutes in your cottage, I had the sense that the people taking care of you were all pretty caring. Yet after being jacked around so many times by social workers, lawyers, and therapists, I didn't trust anyone. You trust these people, confide in them, and then they leave—or stab you in the back. I have been disappointed more times than I want to remember.

I was also jealous of the people taking care of you and their skills. I saw how you looked at Ellen. I heard about all the sports you were doing with Neil. I saw your photo album. I longed to be one of those adults you had come to love and admire. They all seemed so confident. They didn't lose their cool during emergencies, had tons of energy, and knew which words to utter when a kid was down.

Some of the staff talked to me like I was an idiot. Others just seemed uncomfortable dealing with parents. It was probably more fun for most of them when we weren't around.

It was also hard coming to Highland Hills because of what it provided: beautiful grounds, lots of sports equipment, computers, TVs, Nintendos, nice furniture. You had it better than me. I never had any of that stuff. I never got the kind of clothes they gave you. I never ate as well. I never had a chance to take horseback riding lessons or attend summer camp. I never had people taking care of me who weren't either abusive or alcoholic.

Highland Hills appeared to me like an upper-middle-class institution. Most parents of kids living there can't afford to give their kids the same kind of things. A lot of us don't have what you would consider high-paying jobs. Most of us have trouble making ends meet, and some of us are on welfare. Seeing you had reminded me of how much I lacked. Damn it! Why had life been so fucking awful? Was it all my fault? Claire said it wasn't, but . . . Look, I know the psychological mumbo jumbo that goes on in group homes and residential treatment centers is important. I'm sure it's important for you and for me to talk about our mothers. Talking about problems can certainly help, but sometimes people can be helped more by actions. Heck, don't actions speak louder than words?

Instead of just talking to a parent, how about helping them find and be able to afford a better apartment? Instead of trying to bring us along therapeutically, how about occasionally bringing us to the grocery store or dentist's office since a lot of us don't have cars? Instead of getting upset if we can't make it in for a therapy session, how about offering to conduct sessions at our house? Instead of trying to get us into a new therapy group, how about trying to help us with membership at the local Y?

I think sometimes when I missed visits with you or treated you unfairly, it had to do with my anger at my own life. I would take it out on you. Jesus, Gus, I'm sorry, honey. I do love you. It kills me that I've caused you so much pain. It wouldn't surprise me if you never wanted to see me again. But I'm not gonna quit on you! I'm beginning to sort out how much stuff visiting Highland Hills brought up for me with the help of my new therapist, Marge. I'm finally seeing the picture of our lives with some clarity. Marge is good. I'm not as angry as I once was, nor as brittle. But I still have a long way to go.

Interestingly, I got a package from your therapist, Ellen, last month. It was good to hear from her. I wasn't sure how she felt about me. I know she couldn't have been too happy about my failure to make it with you after all the effort she put into helping us. She talked about exciting changes at Highland Hills. She said the program was changing from being "kid centered" to "family centered." A booklet the agency put together explained what this meant. It really hit home. It spoke about many of the things I just mentioned. It also explained that when residential treatment was first offered to abused and neglected kids forty or fifty years ago, the idea was to work primarily with the kids. Group homes and residential treatment centers took in emotionally disturbed kids, fixed 'em up, and then sent them home.

Not too much attention was given to the parents. Well, I guess the results weren't terribly impressive. It didn't seem to matter how well a kid was doing at the time of discharge if the kid was returned to a family that hadn't changed too much. If the family hadn't changed, the kid usually ended up out of the home again, often in worse shape. Big surprise.

So it makes sense that places like Highland Hills are now becoming more focused on the families. They will be looking to form partnerships with each child's family. They want parents to spend big chunks of time hanging out where their kids are living, and being involved in all aspects of their kids' treatment. She said they've started to do this, and the results have been great.

I guess at Highland Hills you now have parents and siblings coming in and interacting as integral members of the residential community. Ellen talked about one mother who makes a mean pizza and a father who's been dazzling the kids with his basketball wizardry. The Halloween event sounded like a gas, as well—parents, siblings, big brothers and sisters, and staff all dressed up for a big party. That's the way it should be. I remember walking into that place and feeling low. As nice as people were, I often felt like they were talking down to me. They were the "good guys," and I was the "bad parent." I used to think, *"The hell with them, I'm not such a shit. Get to really know me and you'll see."* But other than receiving standard therapy, there was no opportunity to get to know the people who were taking care of you.

Yet, I would think most parents, including this lady,

would be nervous as heck about interacting so much with the enemy—the people who judge us and are in control. 'Cause let's face it, as much as parents and staff become buddy-buddy, they're still the ones in control. Parents like us have usually been in the "system" a long time. We're not used to having much of a voice. We're used to being told what to do. So we're a little wary of authority.

The changes going on at Highland Hills are good but make me nervous. They involve parents really needing to trust the staff. *Trust* is a word that's disappeared from some of our vocabularies. But I think they're moving in the right direction.

Gus, if you feel like writing back, I'd like to hear how this parent stuff is going.

Well, kiddo, I think I've written about as much as I can. So what's next? I guess it's up to you. I want back in. I mean it. I know I've disappointed you as many times as a pig oinks, but I'm your damn mother and I ain't giving up. Not now.

I've been through hell and back. I've had one awful life, and so have you. I wouldn't be surprised if you never want to see me again. But, Gus, that's not how this story is supposed to end. We've both worked too hard for it to end with us apart.

Kid, I love you. I think about you every day. Sometimes when I'm alone, I cry and remember the bad stuff, the abuse, and I want to vomit. But every now and then a nice memory floats to the surface. One time, when you were four, I took you to the amusement park. You couldn't get enough cotton candy. And when we got home, I caught you trying to eat real cotton dipped in mouth-wash. Yecchhh!

I love you, son. You're my boy. I'll be calling Ellen next week to see where things are at. Hang in there.

Love,
Mom

EIGHT

HELLO, FAMILIES

The letter from my mom was more like a freakin' book. It was one of those "I'm sorry, please forgive me" jobs. Screw her! After all she's put me through, the bitch expects me to welcome her back with open arms. Hell no! Not this time. Not this boy.

"Gus, you ready for dinner?"

"Go to hell, John! I ain't eatin' tonight."

John: What did you say?

Gus: I said, fuck off, asshole . . . I ain't eatin' tonight!

John: Look, I don't like the food much, either. Let me close the door so we can talk about this without everybody hearing.

Gus: John, get the hell out of here. I just want to be alone.

John: What's that?

Gus: A goddamn letter from my mother.

John: Jesus, it goes on forever.

Gus: That goddamn bitch. Who the hell does she think she is?

John: Man, you've been through so much.

(Gus grabs his pillow and begins pounding it)

Gus: I hate her! *I hate her!* Drop dead, Ma. You bitch! Go get yourself another fuckin' drink! Leave me alone. *Leave me alone!*

(Gus breaks down. A few minutes later...)

Gus: I hate crying in front of people.

John: Take this tissue. You've got reason to scream and cry.

Gus: Yeah.

John: Man, your life is more up and down than a yo-yo. That really sucks.

Gus: Hey, could we talk about this later? I just want to be alone.

John: No problem. I'll come back later and check on you.

Gus: Thanks.

Sometimes I just want to die. How much can a kid take before he should call it quits? I've done it before, you know. Never wrote about it. No, not suicide. I guess it would be hard to write about that. Self-abuse. A few times I've taken a razor blade and made cuts on my arm. I just couldn't take the pain *inside* anymore. The pain was like a foreign entity that lived in my innards, and there was nothing I could do about it. Life truly sucked. I had no control. I was being jacked around by everyone. I felt hopeless. Cutting my arms gave me some control. It let me see the pain—the old inside-out move. I now use words instead of a blade. It's a much better choice.

I think back to those periods every time my life gets turned inside out. I was lucky I had good people around to lead me through the dark. I've learned a lot about the power of support. People need people. I've heard there's a corny song about people needing people, but it's true. I think most depressed, self-abusive kids feel lonely and unsupported, even if they're living in a group home full of people. If you work with kids, be there for them. Don't let the acting out scare you away. Every kid in a place like this is crying out for attention. Make sure they get it.

Christ, Mommie Dearest is back. God, am I ready for this? Hey, at least I didn't put my hand through the wall. I'm doing better on the anger front. I did trash the pillow, however. God, I really miss my mother. I try not to think about her, but she's always there. I've kind of been praying for her to come back (not that I've admitted this to anyone). But now that she's thinking of returning, I want to kill her—talk about ambivalence! Ah, hell, guess this week I'll be doing overtime with Ellen, or El Shrinko, as I now call her.

I'm hungry, but before I run to dinner let me mention a little bit about the family stuff my mother was talking about, because it is important. The new approach of working with families at Highland Hills seems to be making a difference. I actually think it may result in some kids going home quicker. (*Maybe this new way could even help my mother.*) On Tuesday nights, Mr. Spinelli, Vinny's grandfather, comes and hangs out all evening. Occasionally, he cooks up a mean pizza. Every Saturday, Jack's mother and his two little sisters spend the day. Jack's mom, Rita, seemed pretty nervous when she first started coming. She hardly spoke at all. I think some of the behavior she saw really blew her away. For a while she even stopped coming. But she's been back for three or four months and has really loosened up. She's actually a pretty good artist; she's been drawing some funky pictures for the kids.

At first, some of us kids didn't love the idea of parents spending time here. For me it was like a kick in the face. Every time a parent walked through the door I was reminded of the fact that I didn't have anyone to visit me.

The counselors spoke with us about this. They said those who don't have family members to visit with might feel bad, but that this was a new approach they wanted to try. They said the goal was for each kid to have a "visiting resource" and in time they hoped all of us would have someone coming in on a regular basis—either a new or old family member, big brother, relative, or teacher.

Mostly it's worked out okay. Some of the kids who don't have families even look forward to visiting with the families who do come in. And I think it must be a nice feeling for the parents to be chummin' with the staff. It looks like they're all one big, happy family, at least most of the time. Last week, however, there was some trouble. Gordon Fletcher walked up to Hank Greeley and punched him in the face. At first, no one could figure out why. I knew because I wanted to punch him, too. Hank's mother had spent all afternoon cooking with us. She was really nice. Gordon and I were jealous as hell. Neither one of us even sees our mothers anymore. Hank made the big mistake of having a caring mother. The bastard.

Not only are parents constantly coming in and out of the place, but we're having some wild events as well. On Halloween, when many of the parents, big brothers and sisters, and staff dressed up and we had a bodacious party, Billy's mother came as the executive director. Pittsy never looked so good! We've had some group softball games with barbecues afterward, too.

The parents also have a weekly support group. At first, some of the kids were ticked because instead of going to an activity, we were recruited to help pick the parents up. What a bore. But when it was explained, it was hard to argue about. I guess a lot of parents don't drive or have other kids to take care of. In the old days, according to Ellen, places like Highland Hills would offer the groups but expect parents to make it in on their own. A lot of them simply couldn't do it. Now, we pick up the ones who live close, and some of the staff members help watch their kids. Since the Hills started doing this, a ton more parents have gotten involved. And it's not just the driving, it's the feel. The place has become like one large community with everyone a valued member.

This approach makes a lot of sense. You wonder why it took so long to begin the changeover. But hey, don't think we're talking about utopia here. Some people initially doubted the wisdom of it, and kinks had to be worked out. I overheard some of the staff really bitchin' when the family-centered thing was first introduced.

"Man, it's hard enough taking care of the kids! We don't need parents hanging out stirring them up."

"I'd have no idea what to say to a parent."

"Are all the kids in the family coming in? They're hellions!"

"It'll be weird setting limits with a kid when his mother is here."

"What if a kid needs to be restrained? How will the parent handle that?"

I think it took a lot of training before people started to feel comfortable with the idea.

One thing they do now that blows me away concerns consequences. In the old days, if a kid screwed up, the staff dealt with it. End of discussion. Now, if a kid screws up—and I'm not talking minor infraction here but assault, running away, stealing—the staff get on the phone and, together with the parent, mete out the consequences.

Some of the troops didn't like this wrinkle in the suit. In the old days, home and residence were usually regarded as separate. Where you screwed up is where you faced the music. Now, it doesn't matter. They're all working together. It really cuts down on the fine art of "splitting" (one of our favorite pastimes).

A couple of weeks ago two of the kids were talking about running away. The rumor spread like wildfire. When the staff found out, they got creative. Instead of talking to the two and then putting them in "close supervision," the staff called each kid's mom and then the kid spent ten minutes on the phone with her. After that, they didn't go anywhere. Surprise.

The staff members say they now work as "partners" with our families. It's a big reason Highland Hills is junking its major behavior management tool: the level system. From what I understand, most group homes and residential treatment centers use level systems in which kids receive points for good behavior. The points are tallied, and kids are assigned a level based on how well they did. Each level allows kids certain freedoms and privileges. Earn the maximum number of points and you make the highest level and have the most fun. Screw up and you drop levels and have fewer privileges.

I think most staff members like using a level system. It helps maintain consistency and structure, and is a good feedback mechanism for the kids. Some staff members like carrying the clipboards that hold the point sheets. It's a power thing. From what I've overheard, a lot of folks are unhappy about doing away with the level system. In fact, Joan and Barbara were arguing about this last night. Joan felt that having levels reduces power battles between staff members and kids. "We don't tell teenagers what they can and cannot do. They earn what they get. If a kid's upset with not being able to go somewhere, I tell him, 'Hey, that's the level you earned, don't blame me. Earn a higher level. Make better choices.' Without a level system, we'll be arguing with the kids all day. I think it would be chaotic. Things generally run smoothly now. Why change it all?"

Barbara countered: "You're right, things do generally run smoothly. But is that our goal, to have a smooth-running program? Our goal is to get kids home or to less restrictive environments. That's why we're making all these changes. Does a kid's family use a level system? Hell no. If a kid is home and wants to go somewhere, his mother has to decide if that's okay. And that mother won't be checking any darn clipboard to see if her kid is on the right level. No, the parent will make the decision based generally on how her kid has been doing and what that kid can handle."

Joan: And what if the kid doesn't like her decision and they get into a big fight?

Barbara: Then they'll have to work it out. And we can help them learn how to better communicate and respond appropriately when tensions arise. We will also support them by doing the same thing here. If we start dealing with the kids like their parents do, and vice versa, hopefully we'll all move ahead much faster. We shouldn't be shying away from conflict. Kids will still be able to earn freedoms and privileges under the new family-oriented system. It just won't look and feel so artificial and regimented. It will be more humanistic. No more clipboards—just direct communicating.

Joan: I see your point, but I don't know if it will work.

Barbara: Hey, we're all a little nervous. But it's a step in the right direction. I read somewhere that there is no correlation between how well a kid is behaving at the time of discharge and post-discharge success. The only thing that seems to matter is how supported the kid and family are after discharge. Kids will feel more supported if their families use behavior practices that mirror the program's techniques.

Joan: We'll see.

At first, I was upset to hear that the level system was being abolished. It was something I could count on. I knew exactly what I could earn, and I liked the constant feedback. I wasn't so sure I wanted the staff members using more discretion when it came to what I could or couldn't do.

Yet I never liked the way some of the staff members used the level system. They frequently held it over our heads. Some seemed to get off on carrying around the clipboard and marking down our points. At times it really felt like "us versus them."

"Keep it up and I'll drop your level."

"Fuck you, asshole!"

"Okay, I'm dropping you!"

"Eat mine, prick."

Also, some of the kids actually seemed obsessed about the points they were earning and the levels they were on. And I think some kids improved their behavior just to earn the privileges of the higher levels but didn't really get any better; they just gamed the system. I'm no shrink, but I think change should come from the inside out. A place like this should get you to feel better about yourself, get you in touch with why you act the way you do and motivated to change faulty ways of thinking. With levels, kids get so focused on them the "work" often takes a back seat.

And finally, the kids who often act out—the off-track dudes, as Ellen refers to them, being partial to the train metaphor, although I clearly have a different association with it—often languish on the lower levels forever. For these poor souls, I think the level system only reinforces the bad feelings they already harbor about themselves. Think about it: a troubled kid comes to one of these places already feeling horrible about himself and then he finds out that he's the worst of the bunch—Mr. Low Level, Mr. Bottom-Feeder. What can this do to his already shaky self-esteem?

If I ran one of these places, I wouldn't use a level system. But if I used one, no kid would stay on a low level for long. I'd keep in mind what Ellen says about off-track dudes—that we're like powerful trains and that all great trains get off track from time to time—and I'd have individual incentive programs so they'd be rewarded for trying harder based on where they were at. Then they wouldn't wake up every day feeling like the biggest loser. Instead, they'd wake up with hope.

I'm nervous about losing the level system, but I think this program is heading in the right direction. Everything they're doing seems aimed at bridging gaps and creating "interlocking partnerships" among the professionals and parents (I stole a handout Ellen produced for the staff, and picked up some cool terms).

Hey, even though I spend a lot of time looking out for number one, I do recognize and appreciate change that benefits us all. Having everyone communicating and working together is great. As a veteran of the social service system, and one sharp dude, I know what happens when people do their own things and communication is weak. I also know what happens when there's an imbalance of power. In a strong, equitable community, power doesn't get misused as there are too many checks and balances. In our new residential community, everyone has a voice. What they're doing here at Highland Hills is putting everyone on the same page and not making assumptions about people.

Troubled dudes, like yours truly, are troubled for a reason. Usually, it's because we come from homes that were chaotic, neglectful, abusive, and inconsistent—to name a few of their less desirable qualities. So we enter the system without a clue as to what good care is all about, and foster care and residential treatment are supposed to provide the answer. However, the answer gets muddled if profound differences continue to exist between our homes and the places that care for us. And where there's muddle, there's too much crap to process. It drives us crazy when we have to choose between home and center. When programs and families really start working together, we begin to get a feel for "right" and "wrong," "good" and bad," and can finally make sense of the world.

Ellen, who's been a residential therapist forever, talked to me about this new process. She said that when she first started, if a parent didn't come to see her the parent would often be labeled "resistant." She now realizes how wrong she was to think this way. For the past eight months she's been doing a lot of home visits and connecting with parents she had written off.

I think she's actually becoming obsessed with trying to help families. Last week while I was in her office, she got five phone calls. (You'd think the lady would have the professionalism to put her phone on Do Not Disturb.)

The first call was from the YMCA. Ellen was trying to get some of her families discounted memberships.

The second call was from St. Augustine's Church. Ellen was asking what kind of programs they run. If more families got more support from their local church, there would probably be fewer kids in out-of-home care.

The third call was from some kind of employment development agency. Ellen wanted information about their services to pass on to families.

The fourth call was from the local health clinic. She was asking whether they took Medicaid, had a sliding scale, and offered sex-ed counseling.

The fifth call was from The Mighty Clipper. The time for her cut and perm was changed.

I guess if you put two and two together you can see Ellen

is starting to focus big time on "out-of-office therapy," as I call it. Sounds pretty good.

Conservatives want to build more prisons and get tough on crime. Frankly, I think building more boys' and girls' clubs and transforming residential care centers to better integrate parents into programs would have far greater impact on reducing society's woes. But who listens to a thirteen-year-old kid with zits?

The new integration of parents into the program at Highland Hills seems promising, although it's resulted in some behavior changes and adjustments. For instance, some parents have become overbearing. Carl's mother calls all the time and wants to be involved in everything. Carl wipes his ass wrong, and she wants a call. The lady may be trying to compensate for past mistakes by getting superinvolved. If so, God bless her, it is better for her to be too involved than the alternative. With help from the staff and her program therapist, she'll probably tone down.

Because of her lack of self-confidence, at least I don't think my mother would become this overbearing. Thinking about my mom getting back in the picture and hanging out in my cottage makes me nervous. As much as I want to try it (but this will be her last chance, damn it!), I wonder how she'd get along here.

The positive changes going on at Highland Hills make me think I should maybe give my mother another chance. She's had a pretty tough life. At least this new approach might be more supportive for her. I don't think it would be easy for her, though. No matter what she might say on the outside, on the inside she'd be intimidated and questioning whether she could care for me as well as the Highland Hills staff. She's always been pretty insecure. I think a lot of the parents come in like that. Can you blame them? They probably have little reason for confidence. Most have led pretty hard lives. They are also used to coming in for therapy appointments where too much of the focus is on what they're doing wrong. Still, with this new approach parents do feel more accepted, and some begin to enjoy real success with their kids.

Having parents come in can also cause the kids to act out, especially before their parents arrive. They are probably afraid their parents won't show, or might not fit in and so prove to be embarrassing. I think some kids are also afraid they won't be able to control their own behavior in front of their parents. They may also be nervous about showing affection toward a staff member, wondering how their parent will react to seeing these relationships.

And then there are the kids (like 100 percent of us) who love but still struggle with feelings of anger and resentment toward their folks. These kids don't know whether to play a game with their parents or throw spaghetti in their faces. In reality, each one of us harbors a myriad of conflicting feelings—and they can change with the wind. We all need time to work through our family problems and conflicts. Because we come to residential treatment after years of problems, there are no quick fixes. But having more interaction with parents in the residential care setting can provide more opportunities to work through the problems and conflicts.

Speaking of fixes, Highland Hills is also doing something new to make sure kids and their families do well after kids are discharged: aftercare. Now when a kid leaves, the kid and his family continue to receive support from the agency. They continue to meet with their program therapist, can attend groups and events at the program, and can call the program for support or crisis intervention. I think this makes a lot of sense. It's not like we're all "cured" when we're discharged.

Discharges themselves can be difficult for those of us who have been living in residential settings a long time. Since I've been at Highland Hills for quite a while, when it's my turn to leave I'll be ecstatic—but anxious as hell. It will be weird and scary waking up without all the structure and support this place provides. It will be hard adjusting to anything else. It doesn't surprise me that some kids don't make it after being discharged from places like this. I bet many of them didn't get enough support after they left. The aftercare they are now providing at Highland Hills will help with that. It seems like a new day is dawning around here.

NINE

ACTIVITIES, SELF-ESTEEM, AND THE GLOBETROTTERS

It's 8:00 p.m., and Neil, the activities director, is walking slowly to his car. It's been another long day, but tonight he won't be leaving as scheduled. Instead, he'll be sharing the story of the St. Jude's Globetrotters with us. The story is a true account about the magic of basketball, self-esteem, feeling connected, and the human spirit, although the names of people and places will be changed. The Globetrotters left an incredible legacy. To this day, their accomplishments remain an inspiration to those who knew them, because they opened up eyes and changed the way many people viewed kids in residential treatment.

I've heard the story a few times now. Afterward, I feel as high as a kite. There are quite a few messages one can draw from the story, so that's why I am going to ask Neil to tell it.

"Yo, Neil. Stop for a second."

"What do you want, Gus? I'm really beat—can it wait until tomorrow?"

"I've got my tape recorder primed and ready. All I need is for you to sit down at that bench, relax, and tell the story of the Globetrotters."

"C'mon, I just finished five hours of softball. I'm smelly; I'm hungry; I'm whipped. I'm not telling the story."

"But, Neil, it's for the book I'm writing. You've told me over and over to make something of my life. Well, this is what I'm doing. People should hear the story."

"Can't they hear it tomorrow?"

"Carpe diem! Live for the day! Isn't that what you preach? I'm here, man. I'm ready."

"Oh why, dear Lord, did you make me such a soft touch?"

"Great. We can sit down over there, under the street-light."

"Testing. One, two, three. Testing. One, two, three. Okay, all set. Ladies and and gentlemen, Neil Perry and the story of the Globetrotters."

"I can't believe I'm staying here to do this."

"Just tell the story."

Tape recorder on.

"Ten years ago, I was working at a large residential treatment facility in the Northeast called St. Jude's Home. There were about ninety kids living there due to various forms of abuse or neglect. I was the activities director. It was my first big-time position. Prior to moving into that role, I served as a child care worker for two years.

"The residential director was a big guy named Ted O'Leary. Some people had the nerve to call him Ted, but most, like me, called him Mr. O'Leary. A brilliant guy, he intimidated the hell out of me, but he was a great boss. He knew I was a fireball of energy with a modicum of talent. I'd bother him all the time with new ideas and he'd never shoot me down. Sometimes, of course, he'd make it difficult. Yet I always enjoyed the interchange. It was like a game we'd both win, as well as the kids.

"Well, one day I walked into the mail room and checked my box. *Hmm, a letter from the Boy's Club. Wonder what they want.*

Youth Basketball League
Friday Nights
Looking for New Teams
Call: Steve Kelly at the Boy's Club

"Basketball league. That was a laugh, since basketball wasn't played very often at St. Jude's. St. Jude's didn't even have a gymnasium, only an old auditorium with a low ceiling and a large stage—a real piece of work. Opposite the stage, maybe ninety feet across, hung one basketball hoop. The floor was green-speckled linoleum. Hard metal screens covered the long, narrow windows that draped the sidelines. The walls were nicked-up wood panel. Pine boards with slats, painted brown, were used to enclose the four old-fashioned radiators that were spaced along the walls. Four metal, institutional-looking double doors loomed in the corners. We affectionately called this place 'the gym.'

"Besides not having a real gym, basketball was a game that the kids here simply couldn't handle. We played a lot of kickball, tag, and dodgeball, but as a rule, basketball meant problems. No one ever wanted to pass the ball; kids would overreact to being touched and they'd fight; and most lacked knowledge of the game and the skills to enjoy it.

"With this in mind, I approached the nearest receptacle to dispose of the notice. As I got closer, a little spark in my brain touched off something familiar. *Wait,* I thought, *our own basketball team. That would be a heck of a challenge. If I could pull it off, it would be great.* I loved a challenge, still do.

"So off I headed for the big guy's office to get his blessing for starting the team. Of course, we would need uniforms and equipment, which would cost money, something social service agencies don't have much of. And fortunately, Mr. O'Leary controlled the dough.

"The bum, he bought it. Gave me the green light without a whimper. *What have I gotten myself into this time?* Not only was basketball a game seldom played at St. Jude's but I knew little about it. Although I was a jock, basketball was never my game. Nevertheless, that afternoon I called the Boy's Club and spoke with a guy named Steve Kelly. He was in charge down there. He was really supportive of St. Jude's entering a team. He sent me consent forms and promptly registered our as yet unnamed team.

"Some of my colleagues thought starting a team was nuts. Others thought it was a great idea. A few wondered if I could get enough kids to play without killing themselves. I wondered about the same thing. I sent tryout notices to all six residential units in the building. Twelve kids generally lived on a unit, two of which were for girls and the rest for boys. Seven kids straggled in to the tryout. Big surprise.

Two of the kids, Hector and Pedro, ages eleven and twelve, respectively, were great athletes. John, eleven, was tall, blond, and coordinated. After that it was slim pickings. One boy, Nate, was the most hurtin' kid I had ever worked with. Due to his self-abusive, aggressive, and destructive behaviors, he required a lot of physical restraint, and he was not averse to dropping a load during the process. He also liked to masturbate—a lot.

"The first thing I did was have them sit on the stage and come up with a name for the team. The only one they could think of was Globetrotters. So we became the St. Jude's Globetrotters, which had a nice ring.

"That first practice turned out to be like most of the others: simple, loud, and tense. I didn't know any drills, and due to poor self-esteem the kids were pretty anxious about putting their limited basketball skills on display. As a result, I usually had to contend with a fair amount of acting out. The boys would pick on each other, make fart noises, or get in shoving matches. They just hated to look bad in front of anyone.

"We were only able to schedule two practices before the first game. I had assigned each player a position (forward, guard, or center), and we practiced the basics. Although three of the kids were good athletes and one could dribble the ball, none of them knew the game. To keep the practices from getting out of hand, I finished each one with a foul-shooting contest. If a boy could make three foul shots in a row, he'd win a Coke—to be paid later. If a kid was fooling around, he wasn't eligible to shoot. I moved the line in for the younger players. Every practice for the next six years ended this way.

"Prior to the first game, I bought each kid a navy blue Globetrotter's shirt with red and white lettering. On the front was the Globetrotter's name with the globe lettering laid out in a semicircle, and on the back shoulder was each kid's name and number. Man, did they love those shirts. Some of the kids even slept in them.

"Those T-shirts came to symbolize how special their team membership was to these guys. Most kids who come to residential treatment have never been on a team, never felt connected to anything. Five years later, forty-six kids wanted to play for the Globetrotters and Mr. O'Leary reluctantly wrote a check for forty-six shirts!

"The Friday night of our first game I was nervous as heck. I didn't know what to expect. I was going to take seven troubled boys into a rough part of town to engage in a game that had previously been a disaster to play. Accompanying me would be Roger, St. Jude's gym teacher, who didn't know the boys very well. That also made me nervous.

"It was a small blessing that all the games were to be played on Friday nights because in residential treatment centers school nights are often tense. Most troubled kids worry a lot about failing to meet expectations. If you listen closely, a collective sigh of relief can be heard at many centers when school gets out on Friday.

"As I drove my seven anxious guys to the downtown Boy's Club for their first game, a large knot formed in my gut. *What the hell am I doing?* When you work with abused kids coming from chaotic homes, you emphasize structure and predictability. You make sure their living space is neat and orderly. This is what makes them feel safe. When they don't feel safe, they usually act out. Walking into the Boy's Club was like stepping into New York City's Penn Station at rush hour. There were kids everywhere, playing pool, basketball, hanging off pipes, arguing, laughing—it was pandemonium. But it was great. This was their place. This is where they belonged. Could my guys handle it? We'll see. *God help me.*

"Most of the kids were Hispanic, a few were black, and some were white. I looked around trying to spot the people in charge. In the poolroom, I noticed a tall, thin white guy in navy sweats who looked like he had just come in from the back woods. He had a long, straggly beard that was more gray than black, disheveled hair, wore Ked high tops, large, thick-rimmed glasses, and, around his neck, the proverbial whistle.

"'Hi, I'm Steve Kelly. Glad to meet you. We're psyched about St. Jude's entering a team,' he said.

"I soon learned that Steve was an incredible guy, the glue that made the Boy's Club cohesive. With limited resources and a challenging group, he made that place good for the kids. In fifteen years, I've met few people I admire more.

"Steve showed us around the club and helped reduce our jitters, though I remained pretty nervous about taking the boys into the locker room. For kids who have been sexually abused, and some of the boys had, a locker room can be a provocative place. Fortunately, they handled it okay.

"While they were getting ready, I gave them the old Knute Rockne pep talk. Win or lose, I just wanted them to play hard, play clean, and have fun. I had no idea what to expect. Nate, my most troubled lad, was making a lot of weird faces and acting very silly. I kept him close.

"As we walked down the corridor heading to the gym door, I saw my life pass in front of me. *What am I doing here?*

"When the door opened, a deafening noise was the first thing to hit us—whistles, screaming, chatter. Two games were being played simultaneously, side by side, each one on half of the large gym floor. The baskets were along the sidelines. There was very little room for the players and coaches to stand. Spectators were crammed into the top two rows of a folded-up stands system. It was wall-to-wall people. *Oh boy, how are they gonna handle this?*

"Roger and I did our best to keep the boys together until the game started. But we were really cramped and my boys were getting edgy.

"Finally, mercifully, a loud buzzer signaled the end of the first two games. As the teams left the court, the Globetrotters trotted nervously onto the gym floor. Roger stayed with them as I checked out which side we were on. Fortunately, we had wandered onto the right court. The team we were scheduled to play, the St. Francis Warriors, hadn't arrived yet. While we waited, I had the boys practice their shooting. Balls were flying everywhere—except into the net. After a few minutes passed, twelve well-groomed boys wearing bright green tops and shorts with stylish lettering paraded onto the floor opposite the Globetrotters. I could see some of them pointing and laughing at our guys. I think Nate was masturbating at the time.

"In a flash, our opponents were into an intricate, intense lay-up drill. They looked like a machine. The Globetrotters looked scared. I quickly yelled to them to form their own lay-up drill. Somehow, it didn't look the same. We were in for a long night.

"A loud buzzer went off, and the teams were ushered to the sidelines. *Oh my God, we're actually going to play.* I assigned positions to the starters, reminding them that it was 'only a game . . . it doesn't matter if you win or lose . . . an apple a day keeps the doctor away.' I threw out every cliché I knew, and then we put our hands in the middle. I yelled, 'Who's gonna win?' They screamed back, 'We are!' and my starters ran out to meet the Warriors of St. Francis. It took a few minutes for Steve Kelly, who was reffing the game, to get my kids to stand in the right places. The forwards and guards didn't know where to position themselves. Finally, the whistle blew and our first game began.

"Instant chaos. The Globetrotters had no idea what to do out there. I'd yell to the kids to get into their positions, but they were clueless. Some ran with the ball, forgetting to dribble. Before I could breathe, the score was 12-0! I could see the substitutes on the other team laughing at us. *What have I done?* The Globetrotters were bouncing into each other, off walls, and hacking the hell out of the other team. They weren't playing defense, they were playing 'kill the guy with the ball.' Kelly was doing all he could not to call every foul that was committed. I'm telling you, Gus, it was not pretty out there. The score at halftime was 18-0.

"During halftime, I gave a great pep talk. 'Hey, it's our first game. Don't worry, you're all doing great. Remember, if you continue to behave well we'll stop for a snack after the game.' The game was just half over, but it wasn't too soon to be talking snack. I was afraid it could get ugly out there. In certain cases, bribery works.

"It was 24-0 before two unplanned events occurred. The first involved a St. Francis kid being stopped from scoring a lay-up. Unfortunately, the boy had been tripped as he ran down the sideline. I looked over and found Nate wearing a sheepish grin. 'Nate! Get over here!' I yelled. For the next two years, I never let Nate stand more than four feet away from me at any time. The second unplanned event occurred midway through the fourth quarter. Pedro sunk a basket! A twenty-footer from the corner. *Thank you, God.* I thought we were going to be shut out. The game ended with St. Francis 28–Globetrotters 2. It was a dark day in Mudville.

"In the locker room after the game, some of my boys were pretty upset. They hated to lose. Losing and being humiliated was worse. I thought some of my boys might go after the St. Francis kids. I did what I had to do. I promised them extra snacks. It worked. I escaped from the Boy's Club without any casualties. But as I drove them to Rosie's, the local convenience store, they seemed pretty down. I tried to pick up their spirits, but c'mon . . . 28–2, that's bad.

"Back at St. Jude's, I tried to make the game sound better than it was. I didn't tell anyone the real score. I tried to stay upbeat. But secretly I was worried. *Had I made a big mistake? Were these kids over their heads?* I didn't sleep very well for a few nights.

"The next Friday it was just as bad. We played the Holy Rosary Knights. Final score: Knights 26–Globetrotters 4. Again, the snacks bailed me out. But this was getting ugly. I played the two games over and over in my head. Both had been living nightmares. The kids simply couldn't follow my directions and probably didn't understand them. I'd tell a kid to play left forward and he'd go stand behind the key. On defense, they fouled like crazy.

"The following Tuesday I scheduled a 5:00 p.m. practice. At 4:00 p.m. I went down to my activities office and grabbed a large roll of masking tape. I had an idea. I got to the gym and began laying down big X's on both sides of the floor where the forwards, guards, and center should stand. When I was done, I waited for the Globetrotters.

"At 5:00 p.m., they started coming in. 'What are the X's for?' they asked. 'You'll see,' I answered. When they had all arrived, I asked them to stand on the sideline as if they were in a game. I then took each boy individually and showed him his position. However, I no longer called the positions forward and guard. Center remained center.

Forward was now: under the basket on this side (the near side) or under the basket on that side (the far side)

Guard was now: away from the basket on this side (the near side) or away from the basket on that side (the far side)

"I told each player that whichever side he was put on was the side for him to stay on. If you're on 'this side' on offense, you stay on 'this side' for defense—no switching. You just run in a straight line from offense to defense, and vice versa.

"I then told the boys to 'always keep your hands up on defense—never put them down.'

"For the next forty-five minutes, all they did was run back and forth from offense to defense, and practice being in position.

"'Pedro, you're under the basket on this side—go!'

"'Jimmy, you're away from the basket on this side—go!'

"'Hand's up on the defense!'

"'Offense . . . defense . . . offense . . . defense . . . Go!'

"'John, go play center!'

"'Hector, go in for Pedro. He's under the basket on that side—Go!'

"'Defense, hands up!'

"I ran their butts off. I was pleased when they seemed to get it. But would they remember this stuff in the game? I couldn't put X's down on the Boy's Club court. For safe measure, I held another practice on Thursday and repeated the same drill: 'Offense, defense, hands up. Get those hands up!'

"Hector and Pedro could run all day. They had amazing stamina. Hector had suffered lead poisoning as young kid, besides incurring his share of abuse and neglect. He was strong as an ox, a phenomenal leaper, and had the body of a Greek god. But he was intellectually challenged. I worked extra hard teaching him the X's.

"Pedro was a fun, dark-haired and handsome kid with a great sense of humor. He had a big temper but generally kept it in check. He also loved the Red Sox. Extremely coordinated, he was a nifty ball handler.

"John, my light-haired center, came from a tragic background. I'd rather not get into the specifics, but this was one hurtin' and angry kid. Still, he could play and keep his cool.

"Nick, age eleven, had a high IQ and was actually a decent athlete. He was nervous about screwing up so he at first never seemed to give it his all. Sometimes he got teased about his freckles.

"Abner, age eleven, was one of my favorites. A terribly abused kid, he nevertheless had a wonderful disposition. He sported a crew cut and large, thick-rimmed glasses. He tended to walk pigeon-toed and wasn't very coordinated. But he tried like heck. The kid had guts.

"Jerry, age eleven, was Abner's best friend and roommate. Jerry was everything Abner wasn't. Jerry was good-looking, personable, and an okay athlete. He really looked out for Abner. I admired the two of them.

"And then there was ten-year-old Nate. This was one sad kid, the most traumatized boy I had ever known. As the activities director, I spent a lot of one-to-one time with Nate. I felt bad for him. Like many of the kids, he had suffered horrific abuse and was now telling us about it through his behavior. He soiled a lot and often needed to be physically restrained for long periods due to his self-abusive, aggressive, and destructive behaviors. He came perilously close to leaving St. Jude's for a more secure treatment setting on a number of occasions.

"This was my gang. It was a challenging crew. In time, I grew to love 'em.

"Having lost the first game 28-2 and the second 26-4, we anxiously prepared for the third game. On game night, when I arrived at St. Jude's to pick up the boys, I was informed that Nick had tantrummed and been escorted to the Quiet Room, a place in the basement where agitated kids were brought to settle down. On each side of the room, kids sat in cubicles to relax and get focused on returning to their unit. The two near corners of the room had isolation booths.

A child having a tantrum might require some booth time to separate him from the others. The room was manned by one or two crisis workers. It could get pretty loud and crazy down there.

"I went down to speak with Nick, who had apparently tantrummed over a minor issue. Like many of the kids who played for the Globetrotters during the next six years, Nick was scared stiff. He didn't want to fail. Acting out was a way to show this and avoid the situation. Usually when kids are in rough shape you don't take them anywhere. You don't want them acting up more so their problems negatively affect others. But this was basketball, something important. I knew Nick pretty well and felt it would be best to take him to the game even though he had tantrummed. I figured he needed a chance to see that he could succeed in such an endeavor.

"This routine became a common occurrence. I'd come in early on Friday night and go down to the Quiet Room to see which players were having pre-game jitters, in the form of acting out. Rarely would I not take a kid for behavior reasons. Once a kid went a few times, played, and did okay, the jitters would usually go away. I slowly began to learn the incredible impact of the team on the kids. Playing for the Globetrotters, wearing the T-shirt, and being part of the team was intoxicating to these guys who had felt like losers all their life.

"After having gotten shellacked in the first two games, I nervously drove the boys to our third game. *God, don't let us get embarrassed again.* This night the opponents were the undefeated St. Augustine Wildcats. They wore bright yellow uniforms and knew the same fancy warm-up drills as the other teams we'd played. They had one kid, I swear, as tall as Shaquille O'Neal. *Oh boy, it's gonna be another long night.*

"Before the game, while the Wildcats polished their pre-game drills, I used every minute to show my guys where the X's were. I even ran into the Wildcats' zone to show the opposite X's. The Globetrotters seemed to understand. The buzzer sounded. It was game time.

"'Who's gonna win? We are!' the Globetrotters screamed prior to the tip-off. Shaq was jumping for the Wildcats against John. No contest. Shaq tipped it to one of his forwards, and before you knew it the score was 2–0, Wildcats.

"With a minute left in the first quarter, the score was only 6–0, Wildcats. The Globetrotters were staying in position and keeping their hands up on defense. They were playing tough! Then Pedro floated one in from the top of the key. Wildcats 6–Globetrotters 2. *Hey, this ain't lookin' so bad.*

"The score at halftime was 12–4. The final score was 18–8. The Globetrotters had played their butts off. The X's had worked. My guys knew exactly where to play, and they were tenacious on defense. The kids were channeling some of their angry energy into the game. It was working. Early on, it became apparent to me that the Globetrotters was more than a basketball team: it was a chance to feel good, to succeed, to be like the other kids. They were hungry for this. I was hungry for this. Success breeds happiness.

"The next week's practice was more upbeat. The kids knew they were improving. I continued to push the X's at them. 'Offense, defense, offense, hands up…get those hands up!' They were getting tighter.

"The fourth game was against the Mt. Carmel Minutemen, who had finished second in the league the previous year. Prior to the game, I noticed a teacher, Mrs. Dunne, and a handful of other kids from St. Jude's in the stands. *My God, we have fans.*

"I decided to start Nate. He hadn't received as much playing time, and Mrs. Dunne was his teacher. Because he liked to masturbate, I ended up yelling, 'Hands up!' on both offense and defense. The other coach thought I was crazy.

"The score at halftime was 14–8, Minutemen. Hector, John, and Pedro were playing like animals. Hector was guarding a kid four inches taller, yet three times in the first half he had blocked the kid's shot. Once he sent a blocked ball screaming toward the ceiling. He was, as they say, making his presence known.

"Entering the fourth quarter, the Minutemen led 22–14. No one scored for a few minutes, and then John got hot. Boiling hot. He started sinking everything he threw up. Meanwhile, Hector had taken over on defense. He was swatting balls away like flies. With forty seconds to go, the Minutemen led by 2, 26–24. My heart was pumpin' out of my chest. I was screamin' at the top of my lungs for the guys to get in position and keep their hands up. Our fans were chanting, 'Trotters, Trotters, Trotters!' It was wild. With twenty seconds to go, Pedro steals the ball and sinks a layup. Tie score, 26 all!

"The Minutemen inbound the ball. Number seven, the Minutemen's tallest player, catches it and drives for a lay-up. Out of nowhere, Hector flies in and rejects the ball. Nick picks it up and passes to Pedro. Pedro dribbles down the right side and launches a bomb with four seconds remaining. The ball goes in and out. Between two Minutemen defenders, John leaps for the rebound. He grabs it and lets a shot go just before the final buzzer sounds. Swish! Globetrotters win 28–26!

"It was the 100–1, '67 Red Sox all over again! There was pandemonium on the court. The kids were grabbing each other. The fans were pounding us all on the back. We were delirious! To this day, I rank that moment as one of the greatest of my life. I'll never forget it.

"I took the entire team out for sundaes. We had a blast. We marched back into St. Jude's chanting, 'We're number one. We're number one.' That night I made a huge banner describing the game and hung it in the front lobby. I would hang a banner after each game for the next six years. I wanted these guys to remember their successes. I wanted the world to know these guys could make it.

"As the successes mounted, more kids wanted to play. No kid was turned down. They each got a shirt. I would take ten boys to a game. Every Thursday, I'd post that week's participants. By the end of the first season, fourteen kids had joined the team and our record was three wins and eleven losses. It had been a successful year.

"To trumpet our success, we held an awards banquet— a fancy dinner in the gym, catered by the child care staff, for which the kids dressed up. After dinner, we watched slides I had taken of the team and then handed out trophies. I tried to make the trophy presentations as dramatic as possible. The banquet became an annual event. I'd have to wheel and deal with Mr. O'Leary every year to get top-class trophies, but after some good-natured jousting, he'd always give in.

"The Globetrotters became an institution. Every year for six years we fielded a team. In year four, we made the play-offs and finished second overall. The semifinal game was played in front of a packed audience. Over a hundred parents, staff, and kids showed up to root us on. We won that game in the last three seconds when Mike Youngbird sank a bomb from ten feet inside the half-court line. I remember screaming at him to 'pass the ball!' In year five, when forty-six kids tried out for the team, I had to break them into three practice squads.

"Needless to say, when it comes to the Globetrotters I have a lot of fond memories. But more importantly, I learned a great deal from those gutsy performers. I learned how important it is for troubled kids to fit in and feel connected, and how far they'll go to achieve these feelings. I saw kids (who would tantrum at St. Jude's if someone just looked at them the wrong way) get pushed, bumped, tripped, and teased during a game, without any retaliation whatsoever. They all knew that if they acted up during a game they wouldn't play again for a while. In six years of games, I never had a serious be-havior problem. Not one. And I often took some of our most acting-out kids.

"Kids who have suffered abuse and neglect usually feel like losers. People who work with them need to make 'em feel like winners, Gus. Years after the first Globetrotter took the floor, ex-players would return to visit St. Jude's. 'I still have my trophy,' I'd hear over and over. The Globetrotter shirts were worn until the kids literally busted through them. And I still remember the kids proudly showing their teachers and parents the banners with their names on them, which they would get if they played that week: 'Billy Hopkins plays great defense!' 'Danny McNeil scores six big points!'

"After a few years, the girls at St. Jude's got into the action as well, starting a team called the Great Dames. They actually beat the boys one year!

"Gus, my whole orientation to working with troubled kids changed as a result of my experience with the Globetrotters. I know there's a lot of psychological hocus-pocus out there, but for me it all comes down to building self-esteem. The Globetrotters demonstrated how far a kid could travel once he began to believe in himself—and if he felt you believed in him.

"In retrospect, the secret of the Globetrotters' success lay in its universal opportunity for individual success. Any kid who wanted to play made the team, got a shirt, played, made the banner, and received a trophy. In the business, tangible reminders like trophies are called transitional objects, and for good reason: they can energize a struggling soul, years later reminding the individual of prior successes and the talent that lies within.

"Another important factor in the success of the Globetrotters was modifying the rules of the game to fit our circumstances. I've carried this lesson with me. Remember, Gus, the times you've spoken about me not allowing the kids to strike out in softball by telling them, 'It's always spring training'? That's a carryover practice from my Globetrotter days. If kids aren't afraid to strike out, more will want to play and will grow from the experience. If basketball terminology is easier to understand, more kids will come and enjoy it. Kids with low self-esteem shy away from activities they think will cause them embarrassment. They often get labeled resistant, but it's really caution. Being a Globetrotter was made safe in the way that a softball game in which you can't strike out is safe.

"Sometimes, Gus, I'll be driving home at night or lying in bed and my mind will take me back to the St. Jude's gym. I'll remember the kids busting through the doors, with their navy blue Globetrotter shirts, ready to practice. Or I'll see Pedro running up to me, all excited, wanting to talk about our last game. I'll see Hector jumping three feet in the air to block a shot. I'll remember returning to St. Jude's after our first win like conquering heroes, chanting, 'We're number one! We're number one!' And I'll never forget seeing Chris Nipper, at the banquet, walking up to receive his trophy after having had four leg operations but nevertheless playing his heart out.

"Being a Globetrotter meant a lot to the kids, but it meant even more to me. Sometimes in this business we're taught not to expect too much from the children. They come to us with labels and histories that, frankly, make us wonder about their futures. On a daily basis, we try to manage very difficult behavior. Even the best of us occasionally loses hope. The spark inside us that burned brightly when we first started dims or flickers out. For fifteen years, my spark has burned brightly. I have my bad days and bad weeks. But, as they say in *Star Wars* epics, 'the force' has remained strong with me—I think, in large part, because of the Globetrotters. May the force be with them."

"Thanks, Neil. I love that story."

"No, thank you. It was good to remember."

"So, what about the Cokes?" I asked.

"Oh, yeah, the Cokes the kids could earn by completing three foul shots in a row at the end of practice. I was worried about them because I never wrote down who was owed what. But at the very end of the banquet, Pedro, the captain, brought me a note signed by all the players. It read:

> Dear Neil,
>
> Thanks for coaching the team. You don't have to pay us the Cokes.
>
> The Globetrotters

"Each kid had signed it, and it's now framed in my home study. The note became an annual tradition. I loved those guys."

Tape recorder off.

TEN

FINAL THOUGHTS

I don't have a lot more guts to spill. Ol' Gus is ready to call it a day. I'm only now starting to believe that the abuse and neglect I suffered wasn't my fault. Luckily, I've had some damn good people helping me.

I'm seeing my mother tomorrow. I can't think about anything else. I haven't slept since I got her letter. Maybe this time it will be different. Who the hell knows? I do like the way this place is now working with families. And I still love my mother. So what the heck, I'll give it one more try. *God, please, let it work this time.*

Writing this book has been fun, but it's also been painful. I didn't, as they say, leave many stones unturned. But no pain, no gain. (You got to love clichés.)

I wrote this book to help people better understand kids. We're not that complicated. We all want to be loved and cared for. When that doesn't happen, we react negatively. Big surprise. Acting out is nothing more than a message to the world that something isn't right. Kids don't act out because they're feeling good; they act out to get things changed. Sure, kids often need consequences for screwing up, but what's most important is why we act out and the tools we need to do better.

I don't believe there is an entity called a "bad" kid. There are only kids who act "bad" because they've had "bad" luck. That's it in a nutshell. But kids like me, hard-luck kids, grow up believing we're bad. Teachers yell at us. Police yell at us. Parents yell at us. Somewhere along the line, the record needs to be set straight. That's what good residential treatment, foster care, and counseling can do if a troubled kid and his family are lucky enough to receive such help.

From the bottom of my heart, I thank all of you who work with tough kids and their families. As Gomer Pyle, the corny marine from an early sitcom, would say: "Thank you, thank you, thank you!" You don't get paid much. You take a lot of bull. And you never seem to receive the recognition you deserve. But you keep coming back, day after day, month after month, year after year. And a lot of you truly make a difference. I don't know where I'd be today without the Neils, Ellens, and Margarets who have been there for me. Words can't adequately express the love and gratitude I feel toward these people—and all people who give of themselves to help others.

We only go around once in this world. Kids only get one chance at being kids. Help us grow. Help us live. We're worth it.

ABOUT THE AUTHOR

Charles D. Appelstein, M.S.W., president of Appelstein Training Resources, is a youth care specialist, author, and speaker whose primary focus is working with children and youth who have serious emotional and behavioral problems. In addition to *The Gus Chronicles I*, he has authored two other youth care books: *No Such Thing As a Bad Kid: Understanding and Responding to the Challenging Behavior of Troubled Children and Youth* and *The Gus Chronicles II*.

In 2007, he published *Facing the Sunshine: A Young Woman's Emergence from the Shadows of Sexual Abuse and Anorexia*. Subsequently he produced two self-help musical CDs for kids and parents, one of which, entitled *Parent Rapsody: Songs and Musical Mantras for Successful Parenting*, won a Mom's Choice Award in 2010. More recently, he released four training DVDs for professionals and parents. Charlie is currently developing a line of strength-based Possibility Posters to inspire hope in settings that guide children and youth.

From 1987 to 1993, Charlie served as the residential director and treatment coordinator for the Nashua Children's Home, a midsized residential facility for at-risk kids and their families. In 1991, he won first place honors in the biannual Albert E. Trieschman Child Care Literature Competition— essay category, for a paper that was later developed into *The Gus Chronicles I*.

Charlie and his wife and daughter reside in southern New Hampshire. To learn more about Charlie and his services, visit: www.charliea.com